MEASURING THE SOCIAL BENEFITS OF MEDICINE

Proceedings of a meeting
held at Brunel University
16–19 May 1983

Edited by George Teeling Smith

Printed in England by
White Crescent Press Ltd, Luton

Contents

Foreword

George Teeling Smith

The papers in this book were presented at Brunel University in May 1983, to an audience consisting largely of senior executives in the pharmaceutical industry. Each paper was followed by a discussion, and the points emerging are summarised in the concluding chapter. It had not been expected that a consensus would emerge and it is clear both from the individual papers and from the final chapter that none did. However, it is also clear that, despite individual misgivings, the measurement of the social benefits of medicine is inescapably an emergent discipline. Despite the scepticism expressed by some of the speakers and audience, it seems highly probable that, within a decade or so, major therapeutic innovations will often be routinely subjected to an economic assessment of their social value, in the same way as their clinical value is usually systematically assessed at present.

As I argue in my introductory chapter, this trend is likely to be encouraged both by the need to balance the risks and benefits of therapy and by the need to justify the costs of innovations before they are routinely introduced into practice.

If these predictions prove to be true, the present volume could be a landmark in the development of a relatively new field of health economics.

Introduction

George Teeling Smith
Office of Health Economics

There has been a spectacular explosion of therapeutic progress over the past 35 years. The consequent improvements in public health may seem self-evident. Why, then, is it necessary to employ the disciplines of economics and sociology to try to quantify these benefits? This introduction sets out to answer this question. It also looks at some of the earlier ways in which benefits have been quantified, and it discusses the reasons why new and more sophisticated methods of measurement are needed in the 1980s. Finally, it examines some aspects of the challenge presented by the new attempts to measure the social benefits of medicines. In covering this general philosophical ground, the introduction provides a backcloth against which the more detailed and practical discussions in later papers should fall into place

First, then, why do the benefits of modern medicines need to be quantified? Watchmakers, for example, feel no need to prove that the convenience of a precise and portable method of measuring the passage of time pays off. Nor do the manufacturers of television sets or video-recorders feel that they have to justify the use of resources on such frivolous machines for our domestic entertainment. Even the manufacturers of motor vehicles – who are responsible, in a sense, for more than 6,000 deaths a year in Britain – do not publish economic analyses to demonstrate the comparative benefits of a system of fast personal transport. Yet twenty years ago the British pharmaceutical manufacturers felt it important to establish the Office of Health Economics, one of whose earliest objectives was to prove that the social and economic benefits of medicines justified their cost and risks.

There are, it seems, four reasons why therapeutic progress needs to be treated differently from other goods and services in this respect. The first, perhaps most obviously, is that under the National Health Service medicines are paid for by the government using money which it has collected from the public in taxes. In principle, there are two alternative ways of allocating resources in society. The first is the market mechanism, under which individuals pay what they feel appropriate for goods and services which they choose to purchase. The second is through the machinery of a government bureaucracy, when the politicians in power decide in their wisdom how much money to collect from the public and how it shall be allocated between different 'public' goods and services. In the latter system, because no individual choice is involved, there is a special responsibility on government to spend the public's money responsibly. If a private purchase proves wasteful, the individual who has squandered his own resources has no-one but himself to blame. If, on the other hand, the government spends unwisely the public as a whole are the losers. In between parliamentary elections, the public are largely powerless to influence the overall pattern of public expenditure. By contrast, their individual purchasing decisions determine on a day-to-day basis the pattern of private spending.

1

Hence there is a special responsibility for government to prove that it is spending the money it collects in taxes wisely. Although pharmaceuticals represent only one per cent of all government expenditure, in 1983 they are expected to cost about £1,500. Such a substantial sum clearly needs to be justified, and the sort of analysis being discussed in these papers is an important step in such justification.

Second, and perhaps more emotively, pharmaceuticals are competing for scarce financial resources within Health Service spending as a whole. It is now recognised that demand for medical care, at zero or near-zero price, is virtually unlimited. On the other hand, the funds which government can vote for the Health Services are strictly limited. Hence there is an acute problem of allocation between competing demands. The money spent on pharmaceuticals could be spent instead, for example, on high technology surgery, such as organ transplantation or the prosthetic replacement of joints. Or it could be spent improving the care for the elderly or the handicapped. Hence, again, it is necessary to demonstrate that the money actually spent on medicines brings benefits. Moreover, it would ideally be desirable to find ways of comparing these benefits with those achieved by other forms of medical care. These papers will demonstrate the difficulty in achieving such precise conclusions.

A particularly emotive aspect of trying to quantify the benefits from medicines in relation to alternative uses of the funds within the Health Services has arisen recently in the political arena. This is the suggestion that pharmaceutical funds should be diverted to improve the lot of low paid workers in the Health Service. It is hard enough to judge between specific services, but when it comes to arguing that pharmaceuticals should cost a little less and nurses and porters should be paid a little more, economic theory is stretched to its limit. Certainly such politico-economic issues are outside the scope of these papers, but they nevertheless highlight the need to quantify the value of spending on pharmaceuticals.

Altogether apart from the question of cost, there is also the risk-benefit equation to be considered in evaluating the role of medicines. It has been pointed out that similar considerations apply, for example, with motor cars. Roads could be made absolutely safe if all vehicles were prohibited. But clearly this option is unacceptable, and in fact strangely little discussion takes place about the need to restrict road traffic to increase road safety. By contrast, the dangers of pharmaceuticals, particularly since thalidomide, are a continual source of public discussion. Thus the benefits of medicines need to be quantified not only in relation to their cost but also in relation to their risk. This will be mentioned again shortly, when the changing situation in the assessment of benefits is discussed.

Finally, the benefits of pharmaceuticals need to be quantified because there is an extreme view that therapeutic progress over the past 35 years has in reality been largely illusory. This view was originally expounded by the American Dubos,[1] and the theme has been eloquently taken up by Illich[2] and Kennedy.[3] Even a member of the medical profession, McKeown, has cast doubts on the contribution which his own colleagues' prescribing has made to wellbeing.[4] Such therapeutic nihilism may seem so extreme that it can be ignored. However, this is certainly not the case. The medical correspondent in the *Sunday Times*, for example, seems largely committed to a view that medicines are a dangerous irrelevance, compared to the contribution which a better diet and a healthy lifestyle could make to human well-being. Television and radio reportedly pick up and develop the same theme.

Thus there is no doubt about the need to find ways of proving that medicines benefit the public, and that they justify their costs and risks. Twenty years ago this task was relatively easy. The medicines which had been introduced between the 1940s and the 1960s had dramatically reduced premature mortality and the need for hospital admissions. Infections such as tuberculosis, diphtheria, scarlet fever, whooping cough and lobar pneumonia no longer killed children and young adults in their thousands each year. Diseases such as diabetes, pernicious anaemia and hypertension were coming under control and their death rates and morbidity were dropping dramatically. It was a simple task to produce equations which showed that reductions in hospital costs, in sickness absence payments and in deaths of young adults were making an economic contribution far in excess of the cost of the medicines which had achieved these savings. It was possible to argue successfully that pharmaceutical companies should make above-average profits to stimulate further similar therapeutic advances.

Even the dreadful effects of thalidomide could be put into perspective in the 1960s. The 500 children damaged in Britain could be set against the 250,000 child lives saved by modern medicines as a whole. In general, it was still accepted that the obvious progress in medicine justified the risks involved as well as the costs.

By 1983, however, the whole situation has changed. The conquest of tuberculosis, and similar scourges, has passed into history, For the majority of the population TB no longer exists within living memory as the 'chief of the captains of the army of death'. Thus it seems as irrelevant to try to justify pharmaceutical expenditure in 1983 on the basis of the control of tuberculosis, as it would be to try to base a wage claim for the sewerage workers on their conquest of cholera.

However, it is not just the specific examples which are now irrelevant. The whole basis of the argument needs to change. Whereas the medicines developed by the pharmaceutical industry in the 1950s were concerned with preventing premature mortality, those in the 1980s are more often concerned with reducing disability. In other words, Terramycin has given way to Tagamet as the exemplar of a successful innovation. Clearly, it is much more difficult to measure the social outcome of advances which reduce discomfort and disability, than it is to measure the economic effect of reductions in mortality or in quantifiable morbidity, such as the numbers of admissions to hospital.

In addition, both pharmaceutical expenditure and the risks associated with medicines are coming under much closer scrutiny. This means that the equations which try to balance costs, risks and benefits have tended to appear increasingly lopsided in public debate, with too much attention given to the costs and risks, and too little known about the benefits.

As far as the risks in particular are concerned, a good recent example is with the anti-rheumatic benoxaprofen. This was withdrawn from the market in 1982 because it was reported to be associated with 61 deaths in the elderly in Britain. In a specific programme of screening to detect the adverse effects of the compound, the Drug Surveillance Research Unit at Southampton University had earlier recorded three deaths associated with liver damage in the elderly. Two such deaths would have been expected from natural causes on epidemiological grounds. The Unit therefore issued no warning based on an apparent excess of a single death. The point is, of course, that naturally occurring deaths are extraordinarily hard to distinguish from those genuinely associated with the use of medicine. However, the figure of 61 deaths was confidently and repeatedly quoted as a justification for withdrawal of benoxaprofen.

What was almost totally absent was any offsetting measure of the benefits from the medicine. Two letters to *The Times* complained that the withdrawal had been precipitate, and in the opinion of the correspondents even a remote risk of death might be justified by the exceptional relief from pain and by the increased mobility achieved with benoxaprofen.[5, 6] It is evidence of these sorts of benefit in hard quantitative terms which is needed if a proper balance is to be obtained in the assessment of the benefit-risk equation.

Another example where risks were exaggerated and evidence of benefits were too scanty came with the anti-nausea preparation Debendox in 1980. This was pilloried, particularly in the *Sunday Times*,[7] based on evidence produced in a law suit against the manufacturers in the United States. This alleged that the medicine had caused birth deformities in the same way as thalidomide had done 20 years earlier. The outcome of the law suit was equivocal. But more significantly, a subsequent study from Northern Ireland which exonerated Debendox was totally ignored by the *Sunday Times*.

Thus what is happening at present is that 'relief of suffering' medicines are being accused of serious adverse reactions, and no corresponding evidence is available of the benefits which they are bringing. It may be that even if the evidence were available it would not justify even the suspicion of risks. However, in its absence, the case in favour of the medicine goes by default.

Thus, just as there was a need in the 1960s to quantify the more clear-cut benefits of the life-saving medicines of the previous two decades, there is now an overwhelming need to quantify the benefits of 'quality of life' medicines in the 1980s. This is what the papers in this volume are all about. Drawing examples from both pharmacology and other branches of medicine, they discuss the new techniques being developed to quantify the benefits of therapeutic progress.

There are, of course, immense problems involved as compared with the relatively easy task of quantifying the economic benefits, for example, of the antibiotics. One is not looking for benefits which can be presented in money terms. However, the Office of Health Economics has always argued that monetary equations cannot be used to determine health policies. If they were, the optimum practice would be to keep individuals alive and healthy up to the day of retirement and then have them drop dead. Clearly such a policy is nonsense. Increasingly, in other spheres also, the quality of a life is judged to be more important than its mere economic contribution and cost. Hence studies are needed which bring out the contribution of modern medicine to human wellbeing so that in health care, in particular, the benefits can be measured in these terms.

The problem of quantifying the traditionally 'unquantifiable' does not, of course, apply only to health care in the 1980s. No classical cost-benefit equation can demonstrate the value of a municipal Art Gallery or a Public Park. However, in the broadest sense, health care is now competing for scarce tax funds with other such forms of public expenditure. Thus there is a challenge to economists, sociologists and members of the medical professions to justify the resources which health care consumes.

The papers in this volume are a step forward in developing and evaluating the techniques which can be used in such a programme of rational allocation of resources.

However, as an almost final thought, it would be wrong to suppose that the proposed evaluation of new medicines will produce a single answer for a particular innovation. Its benefit-risk ratio also depends critically on how well the medicine is used. Figure 1 shows a matrix, with safety on the vertical axis and 'clinical and social significance' on the horizontal axis. Clearly, any product lying in the bottom part of the matrix is acceptable because it is safe. Similarly, a medicine in the top right-hand corner is still probably all right because its risks will be acceptable in view of its life-saving potential. A medicine in the middle of the top – an important medicine with risks – may still be acceptable. However, a medicine in the encircled area in the top left-hand corner is obviously unacceptable.

The picture is complicated by the fact that a particular medicine can shift around on the matrix depending on how it is used. Chloramphenicol, for example, falls in the top right-hand corner when used against typhoid but shifts to the top left-hand corner if it is prescribed for a sore throat. Benoxaprofen is another classic example of a 'moveable medicine'. For a young

FIGURE 1 **The benefit-risk matrix**

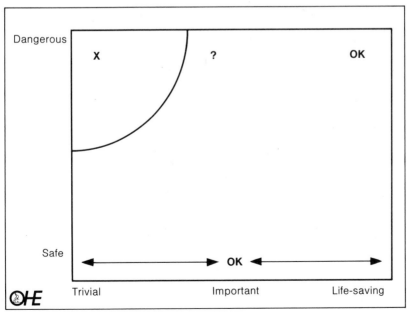

seriously crippled arthritic who has failed to respond to any other anti-inflammatory compound, benoxaprofen lies in the bottom centre of the matrix. In that age group it is relatively safe and it could certainly be important for some patients. On the other hand, if it is given to an elderly patient who would respond equally well or better to an alternative therapy, benoxaprofen shifts into the prohibited top left-hand corner. This sort of consideration adds to the complexity of the analyses being discussed in these papers.

Twenty years ago it was naively assumed that 'more must be better' in the provision of medical care. Few people still believe in such a simple philosophy in the 1980s. Medicine does harm as well as good, and can be inordinately expensive. There is an urgent need to demonstrate more clearly the benefits of medical care in social terms if the health service expenditure and the cost of pharmaceuticals in particular are not to come under increasing fire in the years ahead.

There is no question of a general return to a market system for the provision of medical care so that the public desire to spend on personal well-being could again be expressed in the market place. Nor can it be hoped that the environmentalist lobby will ease up in their attacks on the alleged dangers of medication.

The degree of recent hostility towards medicines is illustrated by the fact that some clinical pharmacologists have actually been advocating what they call 'intelligent non-compliance' by patients. This means that they feel it is right for the patient to stop taking his medicine because he knows better than the doctor what treatment is good for him. In specific cases, in consultation with the prescriber, this is intelligent behaviour; however, when it gets translated into a general proposition that patients are better off without the medicines which have been prescribed for them, it becomes nonsense.

If the health service and the pharmaceutical industry are to survive intact, the measures starting to be developed in these papers must be refined and publicised. Otherwise, at worst, therapeutic nihilism may reign supreme and the very real potential benefits of further therapeutic progress may be denied to future generations.

REFERENCES

1   Dubos R (1960). *The Mirage of Health*. Allen & Unwin.

2   Illich I (1975). *Medical Nemesis*. Calder & Boyers.

3   Kennedy I (1980). Unmasking Medicine. Reith Lectures, published in *The Listener*; November and December issues.

4   McKeown T (1976). *The Role of Medicine*. Nuffield Provincial Hospitals Trust.

5   Duff C L (1982). Opren; balancing the risks. *The Times*; 23 August.

6   Constable G M (1982). Opren; balancing the risks. *The Times*; 8 September.

7   Potter E and Knightley P (1980). Pregnancy Drug Risks; The Facts. *Sunday Times*; 2 March.

Economic assessment of therapy

Michael Drummond*
University of Birmingham

*Present appointment: Visiting Associate Professor, Department of Clinical Epidemiology and Biostatistics, McMaster University, Hamilton, Ontario, Canada

Introduction

In many countries there is concern over the ways in which resources are used in the health care sector. In those countries with a 'liberal' health care system, like the Federal Republic of Germany or the USA, there is concern over rising costs. In countries with a 'socialized' health care system, like the United Kingdom, there is concern over the difficulty in allocating limited resources between competing therapeutic objectives. These concerns have led governments and other health care third-party payers to consider ways of subjecting health care practices to closer economic scrutiny. In the future it may no longer be sufficient to demonstrate that new medicines have a positive clinical effect (when compared to a placebo); it may also be necessary to show that the benefits, in terms of improved health or savings in other health service resources, in some sense justify the costs.

Therefore there has been an increasing interest in the methods of assessing the costs and benefits of health care practices; these are known collectively as *the cost benefit approach* or *economic appraisal* and embrace specific techniques such as *cost effectiveness analysis* and *cost benefit analysis*. In recent years there have been at least two introductory texts on the subject[1, 2], an increased interest from health care policy makers prompting an extensive review of the application of such approaches[3] and a trial of guidelines for appraising options where one of these is a capital scheme[4], plus a rapidly expanding literature.[5, 6]

The purpose of this paper is to give an introduction to the principles and practice of economic appraisal in health care, which, it is hoped, will give a general framework within which the specific applications presented later in this volume can be discussed. The method of exposition adopted is to describe a number of examples of increasing methodologic complexity. In view of the examples relating more specifically to medicines discussed later in the volume, I have deliberately chosen examples of the assessment of other health care practices here, although, in a concluding section, some issues in the application of these methods to the assessment of new medicines are discussed.

Some examples

Before discussing a number of examples of economic appraisal, it is necessary to say a little more about the underlying logic. The main premise is that the resources for the provision of health care are *scarce*, in that there are not, and never will be, enough resources to satisfy human wants completely. Therefore, in choosing to use resources in a given health care activity one automatically forgoes the opportunity to use the same resources in another competing activity. Hence the economist's notion of *(opportunity) cost*; that is, the cost of using resources in a given therapeutic practice is their value in their best alternative use.

Thus the logic is that, given scarcity of resources, health care options should be compared in terms of their relative costs and benefits. This is easier said than done, as the examples to follow will show, although I hope they also illustrate that useful work can be undertaken if the conditions are right. One example will be given to outline each of five forms of economic appraisal, namely:
- cost analysis
- cost minimization analysis
- cost-effectiveness analysis
- cost-utility analysis
- cost-benefit analysis

The first thing to note is that the order of presentation is synonymous with increasing complexity in approach; all five forms involve consideration of costs, but the first form considers only costs. The middle three forms are often grouped together under the term *cost effectiveness analysis*, since they all assess benefits in non-monetary units (in contrast to the final form, cost benefit analysis, where an attempt is made to place money values on benefits). I have opted for this finer division – at the expense of introducing more terminology borrowed from a colleague[7] – since I believe it to be a useful pedagogic device, as I hope will become clear later.

Long-term domiciliary oxygen therapy
Although the main thrust of this volume is to explore new methods of measuring the benefits of medicines, it is worth noting that in some situations a simple *cost analysis* of a new therapy, compared with existing treatment options, can be enlightening. This was the case in the economic assessment of the oxygen concentrator, a new electrically-driven machine which extracts oxygen from air.[8] The new machine was a potential replacement for oxygen cylinders in the provision of long-term domiciliary oxygen (up to 15 hours a day) for chronic bronchitis. The effectiveness of the different methods of oxygen production could be assumed to be the same in this particular case, so interest centered on the relative costs. A major difference between the concentrator and the other methods was that it required capital outlays, for purchase of the machines and provision of workshop facilities. However, the analysis of costs showed that for all but small numbers of patients, where the set-up costs per patient would be prohibitively high, concentrators were to be preferred on economic grounds (see Figure 1).

Even in this simple study, however, a number of methodological issues arise. For example, whose costs should be considered? In this case the concentrator option, although less costly overall, may result in higher costs to patients in electricity charges. (This issue of the *viewpoint* for the analysis, will arise later.) Second, it is clear that the costs of the concentrator option will vary depending (say) on the workshop facilities already available in a given locality. In this case two assumptions were made – alternatives A and B in Figure 1. Finally, the concentrator option, in requiring capital expenditure, results in more costs being incurred sooner rather than later. This

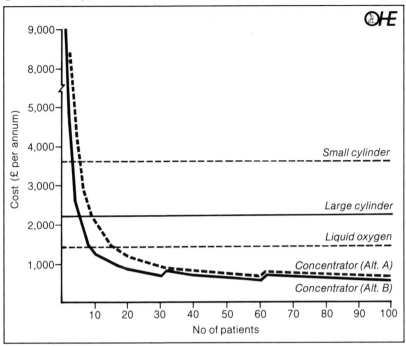

Source: Lowson, Drummond and Bishop, 1981

issue, of the *timing* of resource outlays, is an important feature of the choice since, as individuals or as a community, we are not indifferent to the time profile of costs and benefits. A method, known as *discounting* future costs and benefits to *present values*, is often employed in economic appraisals to make comparisons between costs and benefits occuring in different points in time. (Further details are given in Appendix 1).

Day-case surgery for hernias and haemorrhoids

A slightly more complex situation is one where the effectiveness of the alternative therapies is not known, but can be shown to equivalent by a controlled clinical trial. The study by Russell *et al* is a good example of *cost minimization analysis.*[9] If two therapeutic alternatives can be shown to achieve the therapeutic objective equally well, they can then be compared in terms of costs. Table 1 shows that the day-case hernia patients have similar levels of complications and length of convalescence to the long-stay patients. However, it should be noted that the day-case patients required more district nurse visits. They also required less time in hospital, of course, and therefore a key issue in such a study is the estimation of the cost savings from reduced length of hospital stay. Clearly per diem rates or average hospital costs would be a poor guide. Russell *et al* approached this problem in an interesting way; they estimated the savings under two alter-native assumptions (i) that a move towards day-case surgery would enable a

TABLE 1 **Results of a comparison of day-case and long-stay surgery for patients with hernias and haemorrhoids**

| | Planned length of stay | | |
	Day-case patients	Long-stay (trial patients)	Long-stay (excluded patients)
No of patients	55	56	54
Complications (however slight)			
Hernia	12 out of 32	11 out of 35	17 out of 44
Haemorrhoids*	13 out of 23	6 out of 21	4 out of 11
Length of convalescence			
<4 weeks	8	11	7
4–8 weeks	22	21	12
>8 weeks	14	12	12
Special arrangements made for return home	30	30	32
Average additional expenditure	£4.67	£5.12	£4.33
Preferred length of stay			
Shorter than occurred	2	11	1
Same as occurred	27	41	41
Longer than occurred	26†	4	12
Average No of GP consultations			
Home	0.87	0.55	0.60
Surgery	1.49	1.31	1.39
Average No of DN visits	5.96	1.79	2.07

*Differences almost significant at 5 per cent level.
†Including 17 who would have preferred 24 hours.

Source: Drummond (1980). After Russell *et al* (1977)

5-bedded ward to be closed or (ii) that building a new 5-bedded ward could be averted in the future.

Of course there is the possibility that the freed beds would be used to treat other patients, thereby *increasing* costs overall, although generating more treatment benefits. This places (say) the manufacturer of a new medicine that averts hospital stays in a difficult position. The medicine may offer the *potential* for cost savings but, because of the likely response from the health care system, these savings may not be realised. (See Reference 10 for a good discussion of this phenomenon in the context of day-case surgery.) However, it is still relevant for the manufacturer to demonstrate the potential for cost savings. The question of whether those running the health care system then attempt to attain the savings, or opt instead for increased benefits by treating more patients, is a separate, subsequent, policy decision.

Before leaving this example it should also be pointed out that this is one case where economic analysis was carried out alongside clinical evaluation. There are all too few examples of this, especially in the field of drug therapy.

Treatments for chronic renal failure
In the last example it could be shown that the two therapeutic alternatives

were equivalent in medical terms; what can be done if the medical outcomes differ? In an early *cost effectiveness analysis*, Klarman et al argued that treatments for chronic renal failure have one major objective, the extension of life.[11] If this were the case it would be legitimate to compare options in respect of their cost per life year gained. (The logic here, of course, is that with a limited budget to be devoted to treatment of a given disease, selection of options with the lowest cost per life year gained would maximise the total life extension.) Although now updated by the work of a number of researchers,[12] Klarman et al's work (see Table 2) remains a good example of the kind of results that can be obtained without facing the benefit valuation question directly. However, a logical next question would concern the *quality* of the life years gained. In this case the therapeutic alternative that might be assumed to give the higher quality of life (transplantation) is already the preferred option on simple cost-effectiveness grounds. Nevertheless, this may not often be the case and there may be other therapeutic alternatives which embody a conscious trade-off between length of life and quality of life, eg, chemotherapy for some types of cancer or drugs for hypertension. Clearly, if economic appraisal is to assist in such situations, methods must be developed to tackle the quality of life issues.

Neonatal intensive care

Quality of life issues are of importance in the neonatal intensive care field, where interventions may increase survival rates but that, at least for some survivors, the quality of life-years gained may be poor. Although this topic is still the subject of medical controversy and undoubtedly raises many ethical issues, it is introduced here to illustrate a recent application of *cost utility analysis* (a form of cost effectiveness analysis with quality-adjusted outcomes).

In the study by Boyle et al, valuations of states of health (relative to one another) were obtained from a sample of the population of the city where the neonatal intensive care unit was based.[13] (The detailed methods used to obtain valuations of health states are discussed in other papers in this volume.) It can be seen (in Table 3) that incorporation of the quality adjustment has very little affect on the cost per life-year gained of the cohort of babies over 1,000 g, but has a significant impact on the result for the smaller babies. (This is because the latter cohort contained many babies with poor quality outcomes.)

TABLE 2 **Present values of expenditures and life years gained per member of cohort embarking on transplantation and on centre and home dialysis**

Treatment mode	Present value of expenditures	Life years gained	Cost per life year
Centre dialysis	$104,000	9	$11,600
Home dialysis	$ 38,000	9	$ 4,200
Transplantation	$ 44,500	17	$ 2,600

Source: Klarman et al, 1968

TABLE 3 **Measures of economic evaluation of neonatal intensive care, by birth-weight class (5 per cent discount rate)**

	1000–1499 g	500–999 g
Cost/additional Survivor at hospital Discharge ($)	59,500	102,500
Cost/life-year gained ($)	2,900	9,300
Cost/quality-adjusted Life-year gained ($)	3,200	22,400

Source: Boyle *et al,* 1983

As mentioned above, decisions concerning the level of investment in neonatal intensive care are not an easy matter, but such an analysis can give an indication of the returns (in health terms) for the dollar spent, which can then be compared with the returns in other health care treatment options.

Community-oriented treatments for mental illness

Finally, in some circumstances attempts are made to assess as many as possible of the costs and benefits of options in money terms. This form of analysis is known as *cost benefit analysis*, and was adopted by Weisbrod, Test and Stein[14] in their economic assessment of a new community-oriented programme for mental illness patients (compared to a 'traditional' hospital-oriented programme). It can be seen that even here (Table 4) some costs and benefits are still expressed in non-money terms, but a major contribution of the analysis is to estimate the costs to the various agencies involved, to patients and families, and to the community at large. Figure 2 gives a schematic view of the relevant factors an economist would ideally like to take into account when undertaking an assessment of health care alternatives. As will have been seen from the examples cited, there are many methodological challenges still to be overcome, but it should also be clear that in many cases useful results can be generated without assessing all the factors fully.

Some issues in the economic assessment of new medicines

The examples cited above show that a methodology for undertaking an economic assessment of therapy has emerged and that useful results can be obtained. However, none of the examples chosen relate to new medicines and it is noticeable that while the drug industry, medical researchers and governments have undertaken or sponsored many clinical trials of new medicines, hardly any of these have incorporated an economic dimension. In this concluding section a number of issues concerning the economic assessment of new medicines are discussed.

One key issue is that of *when* to build an economic assessment into trials of new medicines; that is, which medicines should be candidates for economic assessment and at what stage in their development? It is difficult to give definitive answers to either of these questions but, with regard to the

TABLE 4 **Costs and benefits per patient (12 months after admission) for alternative mental illness programmes**

Category	Conventional hospital-oriented programme	Community-based programme
Money costs (C)		
Direct treatment costs	$3,138	$4,798
Indirect treatment costs	$2,142	$1,838
(Falling on other agencies)		
Law enforcement costs	$ 409	$ 350
Patient maintenance costs	$1,487	$1,035
Lost family earnings	$ 120	$ 72
Money benefits (B)		
Patient earnings	$1,168	$2,364
Net money cost		
(C ÷ B)	$6,128	$5,729
Non-money costs		
No of arrests (in group)	1.2	1.0
Suicide (% of group)	1.5	1.5
Non-money benefits		
Days of employment	87	216
Patient satisfaction	significantly higher with community programme	
Clinical symptomatology	significantly better with community programme (on seven of 13 measures)	

Source: After Weisbrod *et al*, 1980

first, those medicines likely to lead to large resource consequences, either because they are of high unit cost or because the number of potential patients treated is large, are obvious candidates. Also, those medicines which could potentially replace another form of therapy (such as surgery) are likely candidates if only because the relative costs (of the drug versus its alternative) are more difficult to assess than if the choice were simply between two drugs administered in the same way.

With regard to the *stage* in a medicine's development at which economic assessment should take place, Drummond and Stoddart argue that this is much more likely to be useful during a 'management' trial, where the medicine is being compared to an alternative therapy when delivered in a practical setting.[15] (This would presumably be in the post-marketing phase.) It was pointed out during discussion at Brunel that this might be rather late from the drug company's point of view, since it may already be heavily committed to the product concerned. It was suggested that the time to assess a medicine's potential for net social benefits would be in the very early stages of its development. Whilst this may be difficult to do given the uncertainties involved, it would represent nothing more than good market research in a world where governments and other third party payers are becoming increasingly concerned about health care resource use.

FIGURE 2 **The relevant changes in a comparison of the economic efficiency of treatments/programmes**

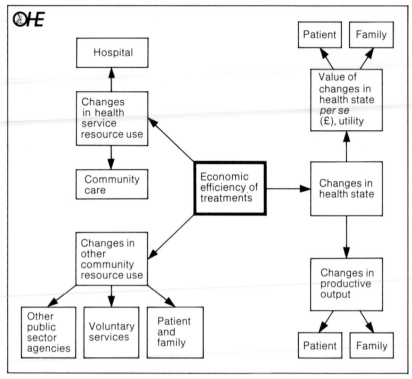

Source: Drummond (1980)

The other major issue is that of *how* to undertake an economic assessment of a new medicine. For example, what should be the viewpoint for the analysis (third party payer or wider?) and how should the study be designed (cost minimization analysis or more sophisticated analytical form?). On the first point, economists would argue for a social viewpoint (in line with the calculus set out in Figure 2 above), although it is understandable that those commissioning much health service research (ie, governments) have a prime interest in the impact of new therapies on their own expenditure. On the second point, it is likely that the early efficacy trials, and indeed the original conception of the medicine, will give some indication as to whether its main economic advantage is in providing a replacement for other, more costly, existing therapies (and hence a cost minimization analysis would suffice) or in confering extra therapeutic benefits, albeit at a higher cost than existing therapy. In this latter case, a cost utility or cost benefit analysis may be indicated.

In either case it is important to take advantage of any clinical trials being performed, particularly those of the 'management' type, in order to collect some of the data required for economic assessment. It is especially important to collect that patient-specific information which would be difficult to obtain later – such as length of hospital stay, length of absence from work and information on patient functioning that may be used in health status index construction. These issues are more fully discussed in later chapters.

The aforegoing discussion indicates that there are many issues still to be resolved, not least that of *whose responsibility* it would be to undertake economic assessments of new medicines, should this be more often required in the future. However, it is to be hoped that this paper, in giving an introduction to the principles and practice of economic appraisal in health care, provides a basis from which the discussion of these complex issues can progress.

REFERENCES

1   Drummond M F (1980). *Principles of Economic Appraisal in Health Care.* Oxford Medical Publications, Oxford.
2   Warner K E and Luce B R (1982). *Cost Benefit and Cost Effectiveness in Health Care: Principles, Practice and Potential.* Health Administration Press, Ann Arbor.
3   US Congress Office of Technology Assessment (1980). *The Implications of Cost Effectiveness Analysis of Medical Technology.* Background Paper No 1, Methodological Issues and Literature Review. Washington, DC.
4   Department of Health and Social Security (DHSS) (1981). *Health Services Management, Health Building Procedures; HN (81)30.* DHSS, London.
5   Warner K E and Hutton R C (1980). Cost benefit and cost effectiveness analysis in health care: growth and composition of the literature. *Medical Care*, 18: 1069–1084.
6   Drummond M F (1981). *Studies in Economic Appraisal in Health Care.* Oxford Medical Publications, Oxford.
7   Stoddart G L (1980). On determining the efficiency of health programs: a user's guide to economic evaluation. *Health Program Review Series.* McMaster University, Department of Clinical Epidemiology and Biostatistics, Hamilton, Ontario.
8   Lowson K V, Drummond M F and Bishop J M (1981). Costing New Services: long-term domiciliary oxygen therapy. *Lancet*, ii: 1146–1149.
9   Russell I T, Devlin H B, Fell M, Glass N J and Newell, D J (1977). Day case surgery for hernias and haemorrhoids: a clinical, social and economic evaluation. *Lancet*, i: 844–847.
10 Evans R G and Robinson G C (1980). Surgical day care: measurements of the economic payoff. *Canadian Medical Association Journal*, 123: 873–880.
11 Klarman H E, Francis J O S and Rosenthal G D (1968). Cost effectiveness analysis applied to the chronic renal disease. *Medical Care*, 6: 48–54.
12 eg: Ludbrook A (1981). A cost-effectiveness analysis of the treatment of chronic renal failure. *Applied Economics*, 13: 337–350.
13 Boyle M H, Torrance G W, Sinclair J C, Horwood S P (1983). Economic evaluation of neonatal intensive care of very low birth-weight infants. *New England Journal of Medicine* 308: 1330–1337.
14 Weisbrod B A, Test M A and Stein L I (1980). Alternative to mental hospital treatment. II Economic benefit – cost analysis. *Archives of General Psychiatry*, 37: 400–405.
15 Drummond M F and Stoddart G L (1982). Economic analysis and clinical trials. *QSEP Report No 34*, McMaster University, Faculty of Social Sciences, Hamilton, Ontario.

APPENDIX 1

Discounting costs and benefits to present values

1 Introduction

It is usually argued that as individuals and as a community we prefer to receive benefits now rather than in the future; similarly we prefer to postpone costs.

The most widely accepted method of incorporating this notion into economic appraisals is to discount costs and benefits occuring in the future to present values. The calculation, which is outlined below, operates rather like a compound interest calculation in reverse and, if a positive discount rate (r) is used, gives less weight to future costs and benefits in the analysis.

2 The discounting calculation

i) *Compound interest*

At an interest rate of 10 per cent:

£100 this year = £100 $(1 + 0.10)$ next year
$$= £110$$
£100 this year = £100 $(1 + 0.10)(1 + 0.10)$ in two years time
$$= £121$$

ii) *Discounting to present values*

Performing the same calculations in reverse:

£110 next year $= £\left[\dfrac{110}{(1 + 0.10)}\right]$ now

$$= Present\ value\ of\ £100$$

£121 in two years time $= £\left[\dfrac{121}{(1 + 0.10)(1 + 0.10)}\right]$ now

$$= Present\ value\ of\ £100$$

3 The discounting formula

At a discount rate of r:

The *present value* of a cost stream occurring in years
0 (now), 1, 2 . . . .

$$= C_0 + \frac{C_1}{(1 + r)} + \frac{C_2}{(1 + r)^2} + \ldots + \frac{C_n}{(1 + r)^n}$$

$$PV = C_0 + \frac{C_1}{(1 + r)} + \frac{C_2}{(1 + r)^2} + \ldots + \frac{C_n}{(1 + r)^n}$$

4 The discount rate

The present value of costs and benefits occuring in the future is obviously dependent upon the discount rate chosen. The choice of discount rate is the subject of methodological controversy among economists. However, in some countries the government advises a discount rate for public sector investments. For example, in the United Kingdom the Treasury currently advises a rate of 5 per cent in real terms.

Also, it should be noted that there is a fair amount of agreement on the discount rate in the literature, most analysts using rates between 4 per cent and 10 per cent. In fact the prudent analyst usually undertakes a sensitivity analysis of his study results to assess the effects of a different choice of discount rate. Often the choice of rate (within the range mentioned) makes little difference to the ranking of therapeutic alternatives.

5 Further reading

This appendix gives only a brief introduction to discounting. Further discussion is contained in Reference 1.

Classic economic measures developed by OHE

Nicholas Wells
Office of Health Economics

The Office of Health Economics has now published 72 papers in its series examining current health care problems. Some of these publications have provided broad philosophical analyses of the changing nature of demand for health care and the problems to which this process has given rise in the face of ever pressing resource constraints operating on the supply side. Others have described and commented on the logistics of health care delivery, with particular emphasis of course on the National Health Service. The majority of the papers in this series, however, have been concerned with specific causes of ill-health. Thus OHE's first report examined tuberculosis – a disease once referred to as 'the chief of the captains of the army of death'. OHE's most recent publication looked at what may in some ways be regarded as the contemporary successor of tuberculosis – coronary heart disease. In the two decades separating these two publications pneumonia, venereal disease, diabetes, epilepsy, arthritis and multiple sclerosis, among many others, have been the subject of OHE's attention. Yet in spite of the diversity of the subject matter under investigation one central aspect has commanded attention throughout – the economic and social sequelae of disease.

In each of its analyses OHE has attempted to quantify the costs that disease imposes upon society. In order to do this it has adopted a number of approaches and these will be examined – along with their shortcomings – in the first part of this paper. Following this review attention will be given to the underlying objectives of these costing exercises. The final part of the paper considers future measurement requirements in the light of predictions concerning the nature of forthcoming therapeutic progress.

Returning to the initial objective, the economic burden of any given disease can be quantified in terms of the impact it has on mortality, the volume of sickness absence from work it generates and the expenditures it gives rise to as far as the hospital and family practitioner services are concerned.

The first of these – mortality – raises many difficulties but was nevertheless employed in OHE's opening forays into the territory of health economics. Whilst the availability of comprehensive mortality records since the first half of the nineteenth century implies that there is no difficulty in establishing the number of deaths attributable to any particular disease – although it might be noted that there is now increasing concern at the apparent inaccuracy of a not insubstantial proportion of official death certificates – the major problem arises in actually costing death, that is, in attributing an appropriate value to life. In its first publication *Progress against Tuberculosis* the approach of OHE was to equate the value of a life to the value of the average *per capita* contribution to the nation's gross national product. In 1962 this amounted to £400. Today the corresponding contribution of each member of the population of the United Kingdom stands at £3,782. Apart from a number of inevitable uncertainties – for example, would a reduction in mortality alone generate growth in GNP (what about the role of the other 'facilitating' factors of production) and can it really be argued that each member of the population makes an equal contribution to national wealth – this observation would appear to suggest that life is ten times more valuable today than it was 20 years ago and thus highlights the difficulties of comparisons over time.

Some economists have adopted alternative approaches to the problem. Gavin Mooney, for example, in his book *The Valuation of Human Life* points out that a popular analytical technique involves consideration of the valuations that are implicit in policy decisions made not by individuals but by persons of authority on their behalf. However, this approach has, perhaps inevitably, generated a broad range of values. Thus at one extreme, it has been estimated that the government's decision at the start of the 1970's not to introduce childproof containers for drugs implied a value of life of just £1,000. At the other extreme, it has been argued that changes in building regulations following the collapse of Ronan Point high rise flats which killed several people were indicative of a value of £20 million. Does this mean therefore that a disease which kills say 1,000 people each year may be costed – from the mortality point of view – at some level within a range extending from £1 million to £20 billion?

One means of circumventing the enormous complexities involved in placing financial values on life is simply to concentrate on the years of lost potential life caused by death. Thus on the basis of the most recently available life expectancy tables, the Office of Population Censuses and Surveys has estimated that mortality among males aged 15–64 years resulted in the loss of almost 1.2 million years of potential working life in 1980. Among the principal causes of this loss were coronary heart disease accounting for 20 per cent, malignant neoplasms 18 per cent and accidents 16 per cent. OHE has certainly employed this type of measure in some of its publications but in the final analysis perhaps it is best to confine attention to straightforward mortality statistics. Employed in an appropriate manner these data can readily convey the significance of disease for specific age/sex groups and as a cause of premature demise.

The second measure of the economic significance of disease is sickness absence from work and OHE has examined this as a topic in its own right on several occasions. Prior to recent legislative changes payment of national insurance contributions by employees and their employers conferred upon individuals the right to claim state benefit payments to compensate for any loss of or drop in earnings during sickness. Entitlement to claim is dependent upon the acquisition of a certificate signed by a doctor confirming incapacity for work. Each year a sample of these certificates is selected and analysed by the Department of Health and Social Security and information relating to spells and days of absence by cause and various claimant population characteristics has been published.

In addition to these data, DHSS also publishes figures showing the cost of meeting sickness benefit claims each year. Consequently, it is possible to calculate the average daily cost of sickness benefit and hence the burden generated by any particular disease. Thus DHSS data yet to be officially published indicate that there were 345 million days of sickness absence in Britain in 1980/81 which cost the national insurance fund more than £1.7 billion. This works out at just over £5 per day of absence and, as an example, it may be calculated that the 26 million days of absence due to coronary heart disease gave rise to sickness benefit payments totalling £133 million in 1980/81.

Inevitably official sickness absence data suffer a number of important limitations. For example, spells of absence lasting 3 days or less are generally excluded from the statistics since benefits are not normally available for such short term absences. Shortfall also stems from the fact that approximately half of the married women who work exercise their right to opt out of the national insurance scheme and so their spells of absence are not recorded. With similar effect a number of other groups such as non-industrial civil servants, employees of the Post Office and members of the Armed Forces – together totalling nearly one and a half million individuals – are partly or wholly outside the scheme. To some extent these and other factors are, however, counterbalanced by the overstatement of sickness days implicit in the fact that DHSS data are based on a 6 day working week.

Qualitative deficiencies also exist alongside these quantitative shortfalls. The medical cause of incapacity recorded on the doctor's certificate, for example, is in many instances just a reflection of the information imparted by the patient about his or her symptoms rather than any specific or verifiable diagnosis. Even when there is an identifiable medical component little can be gleaned about severity: the timing of return to work may be influenced by factors other than the termination of ill health. In spite of these considerations the data are clearly valuable in facilitating calculations of the sickness benefit cost of disease. They also provide a reference point from which the wider economic ramifications of sickness absences from work may be analysed.

The costs borne by companies, for example, apart from statutory contributions to the National Insurance Fund and expenditure required to administer sick pay schemes, are largely dependent upon the nature of the tasks affected by an employee's absence. If for a short period of time they can readily be absorbed by other members of the workforce without disruption to the overall productive effort then few if any extra costs will ensue. If this is not feasible, or if absence is prolonged then additional expenditure will result if the deficiency is made good by hiring temporary replacement labour (at the same time as paying the absent employee sick pay) or by extending overtime working. In 1981 it was estimated by contributors to meetings organised by the Industrial Society that these and other related costs (but excluding company sick pay itself) amounted to approximately £20 per day.

One of the approaches adopted by OHE in this context has been to equate the value of lost production to average earnings. These figures are readily available – the latest information suggests that in Britain in 1982 average daily earnings for male manual and non-manual workers employed in all industries and services amounted to just over £31 – and may be employed in conjunction with sickness absence data. As an example it might therefore be calculated that at the start of the 1980s the recorded annual total of

25 million days of male absence due to coronary heart disease generated £640 million of lost production apart from expenditure of £125 million from the National Insurance Fund.

Of course a 'notional' economic cost estimate of this type is open to criticism. Average wage figures disguise a very broad range of earnings and it can also be argued that the value of employment tasks is not universally represented with any degree of accuracy by received income. But perhaps the principal shortcoming of estimated production foregone values arises as a consequence of the content of the sickness absence statistics themselves. The DHSS data include unidentifiable absences attributable to persons who are unlikely ever to work again and who will continue to receive sickness benefit until they attain retirement age. These individuals cannot therefore be regarded as members of the workforce and converting their days of absence to production foregone values might be deemed inappropriate.

Hospital costs have been another area of major interest to OHE in its evaluation of the financial impact of disease. Indeed, the economics of hospital care has received considerable attention throughout the health economics profession – perhaps more than any other topic embraced by the discipline – and the reason is readily apparent: the hospital services currently cost an estimated £8.5 billion in the UK and have, since the inception of the NHS, consistently absorbed approximately three-fifths of the service's resources. Consequently, there has been increasing concern to ensure that these resources are utilised efficiently and this has been manifest in the undertaking of studies at both macro and micro levels.

OHE's concern in this field has largely been to establish the proportion of the total hospital bill that may be attributed to specific disease. Again the data are readily available and the methodology straightforward. In England and Wales, the hospital inpatient enquiry (HIPE), which is based on a 10 per cent sample of non-psychiatric hospitals, yields data on admissions, lengths of stay and other variables by diagnosis and patient age and sex. In addition DHSS also publishes health service costing returns which detail the expenditures generated by hospital inpatient care. Thus to take once again the example of coronary heart disease, the HIPE indicates that in 1978, the latest year for which detailed information is available, there were 144,540 admissions for the disease and that each admission lasted for an average of 17 days. This yields a total hospital stay of 2.45 million days. If it is then assumed that hospitalised heart disease cases are treated in acute hospitals, an average cost per inpatient day of £38 emerges from the health services costing returns for 1978/79. Drawing the two figures together indicates a hospital inpatient cost for coronary heart disease of £93 million. Official data such as these are inevitably several years out of date but by adjusting the outcome costs by an appropriate amount to take account of price increases it is possible to obtain an up to date costing: in this instance inflation adjustment raises the cost from £93 million to £146 million at 1982 prices.

In common with the measures already described, figures relating to the costs of hospital care suffer a number of drawbacks. Thus there is little information concerning the costs surrounding the inpatient spell. Outpatient consultations, for example, leading to hospital admission and providing for subsequent follow up are available only in highly aggregated form and cannot be linked to specific inpatient episodes. This also applies to other services such as those involved in patient rehabilitation. But perhaps the principal problem lies in the fact that the costing figures are once again averages. In the case of coronary heart disease such averages lead to a clear understatement of the true level of costs. Heart disease patients admitted to medical wards may require a greater number of particularly costly diagnostic tests, closer and prolonged surveillance and more expensive pharmaceutical therapy than patients in other specialties. On the surgical side, coronary artery bypass grafting requiring preliminary investigative arteriography and subsequent intensive care probably generates *per capita* hospital case costs which are markedly under represented by the averages shown in the published health services costing returns.

Focusing on the costs of primary medical care, OHE has adopted an approach which is broadly analogous to that employed for the hospital sector. Information is readily available concerning the total cost of the service – which stood at £743 million in 1980 or 6.3 per cent of the total cost of the NHS – and this is linked to data drawn from the Second National Survey of Morbidity in General Practice. This investigation was completed at the start of the 1970s and indicates, for example, that of the estimated 3,010 consultations per 1,000 individuals, 50 consultations or 1.7 per cent of the total were for coronary heart disease. Assuming this proportion is still valid it can therefore be calculated that this particular disease accounted for £12 million of the resources allocated to the general practitioner services in 1980.

Again, the insufficiently detailed content of available information implies a number of difficulties. It is clear, for example, that different diseases impose dissimilar burdens on the GP service: some will require lengthier consultations than others and marked variation will equally exist in terms of the need for the primary care back-up services. But perhaps of greater significance is the fact that the Morbidity Survey is rapidly becoming outdated. Pharmaceutical innovation yielding new medicines, increasing awareness of the need to monitor patient use of and response to medication and encouragement given to general practitioners to extend their role in matters of health promotion and disease prevention may, along with other factors, have served in some instances to increase the workload of family doctors to levels above those prevailing at the start of the 1970s. In the absence of a further detailed survey it is not possible to be certain of the trends and information provided by the General Household Survey, the only up to date alternative source of information, is far too broadly based to be of any value in this specific context.

One final source of resource expenditure information exists within the family practitioner services – the cost of pharmaceuticals provision. Available data breaks down NHS prescriptions statistics in a way which permits identification of expenditure on broad groups of drugs. However, the extent to which costs can be attributed to specific diseases varies substantially. Thus anti-Parkinson drugs will presumably be used solely for the treatment of Parkinson's disease. Analgesics, systemic anti-infectives and beta blockers, on the other hand, will be employed across a wide spectrum of disease. Heart disease is an example where drugs from a number of different classes may be employed. Thus to the net ingredient cost of preparations acting on the heart – amounting to £92 million in Britain in 1981 – might be added part of the cost of the vasodilators and vasoconstrictors group of drugs. Furthermore, given that raised blood pressure is an important risk factor for coronary heart disease it might be deemed appropriate to attribute a certain proportion of the annual cost of prescriptions for anti-hypertensives and diuretics to the cost of therapy for the disease. Finally, some of the expenditure on tranquillisers might also be included as these medicines constitute an important aspect of therapy for some heart patients. Taken together the above groups of drugs accounted for 25 per cent of the net ingredient cost drug bill in 1981. It might be concluded, therefore, that between 15 and 20 per cent of the nation's drug bill is attributable to coronary heart disease instead of the 9 per cent implied by concentrating only on preparations acting on the heart.

The foregoing therefore constitute the measures OHE has consistently employed to gauge the financial implications of disease. In several instances consideration has also been given to more specific economic aspects – such as the benefits of screening for birth impairments, the economic issues inherent in caring for the elderly demented in community as opposed to institutional settings and the costs of widespread employment of beta blockade following acute myocardial infarction, Nevertheless, mortality measures coupled with the costs of sickness absence and of the hospital, general practitioner and pharmaceutical services have, in spite of their shortcomings provided the fundamental framework for OHE's work in this field. But what has been the objective underlying these disease costing exercises?

They have in fact served a number of different purposes. First, by converting the various impacts of a specific disease to one common, that is financial, form it is possible to gain some impression of its overall burden which can then be judged in relation to other causes of ill health. In theory this might offer clues to the priority that ought perhaps to be given to resolving the morbidity and mortality associated with different disease entities.

Secondly, OHE has shown in its use of these measures that pharmaceutical expenditure is frequently only a minor element in the cost of disease and by broad extension, that the cost of the nation's drug bill, when seen in perspective, is not as excessive as some critics have claimed. The recent debate generated by the Greenfield proposal that generic substitution be applied to prescriptions originating from the family practitioner services is to some extent illustrative of the problem. Thus discussion has focused on the uncertainty concerning the size of the potential savings that might follow the implementation of such a policy with little attempt to place the size of the drug bill in context – to point out, for example, that total government expenditure on drugs in 1981 amounted to less than 6 pence per head of population per day. And, further, that this sum was only one tenth of that committed to spending on defence and represented just one per cent of all government expenditure in 1981.

Within the private sector, the daily *per capita* cost of NHS medicines corresponded exactly, at 6 pence, with average consumer spending on newspapers but was 21 pence less than the average amount allocated every day by each member of the population to tobacco consumption and 50 pence less in the case of alcohol. The need to promote greater understanding in this area is clear from recent survey findings that only one person in five knows that pharmaceuticals account for less than 10 per cent of the total NHS budget. In 1980, the average member of the general public believed that the figure was actually 35 per cent.

A third role of OHE's costing exercises has been to demonstrate that chemotherapy may represent a highly cost effective means of treating disease. In 1980 the average net ingredient cost of a prescription in the UK was £2.37, rising to almost £3.00 if account is also taken of the various dispensing payments made to pharmacists. If it is assumed that each prescription provides, on average, for a course of therapy lasting 21 days, then the cost of chemotherapy works out at just £1 per treatment week. In contrast, data taken from the Health Services Costing Returns for England and Wales and inflation-adjusted to 1980 prices indicate that one week's stay in an acute hospital bed would involve a cost of £334. Of course, it would be misleading to imply that today chemotherapy exists as a straightforward and clearly substantially less expensive alternative to therapy requiring hospital admission in the majority of instances of ill-health. Nevertheless, the development of effective pharmaceutical treatments has in the past generated cost savings by both postponing or avoiding altogether the need for inpatient care as well as by helping to reduce the duration of hospital stay in cases where the latter is deemed necessary.

Finally, and following on from the last point, the measures described in this paper have been employed to demonstrate that pharmaceuticals can generate real economic benefits. Thus in the publication on tuberculosis OHE estimated that cumulative reductions in premature mortality and hospital bed requirements made possible by the development of antitubercular medication had, by the early 1960s, led to savings of £55 million per annum – equivalent to more than half the cost of NHS expenditure on all drugs to treat all diseases at that time.

Updating this economic gain, it has more recently been calculated that the fall in the number of hospital inpatient cases of tuberculosis from 67,200 in 1955 to 6,170 in 1979 may be calculated to have saved – or, perhaps more accurately, spared – £300 million in reduced bed days in the latter year. Combining with this figure the equivalent hospital savings in psychiatric illness, hypertensive disease, pneumonia, epilepsy, bronchitis and skin diseases generates a sum of spared expenditure in the late 1970s of approximately £770 million. This sum was almost identical to the size of the entire net ingredient cost drug bill in England and Wales at that time.

The implication of calculations such as these is that, at the very least, expenditure on drugs is self-financing and that the accompanying economic benefits unquestionably justify the creation and subsequent fostering of an environment which positively encourages pharmaceutical innovation. Yet arguments couched in these terms, whilst clearly valid in relation to the era which saw the development of anti-infective medication, have become less and less appropriate over time. The last two decades have witnessed the evolution of medicines which do not on the whole generate economic benefits because of substantial reductions in premature mortality, hospital inpatient treatment or absence from work. Instead new medicines have increasingly had a greater impact on the quality of life by reducing morbidity and facilitating effective control over the unpleasant symptoms of chronic disease.

The development, for example, of prophylactic therapy for asthma as well as the selective beta agonist drugs which facilitate rapidly effective and convenient control of attacks of breathlessness have greatly improved the quality of life and provided psychological reassurance for many asthmatics. Similarly, the evolution of non-steroidal anti-inflammatory drugs has generated considerable gains for many of the hundreds of thousands of individuals suffering from diseases of the joints and organs of movement (such as arthritis) by promoting greater mobility and pain control. In both of these instances the patient benefits principally assume the form of enhanced well being and social functioning and as such are not as readily quantifiable as those associated with advances leading to reductions in mortality or hospital admissions. This contention holds true in many other areas of pharmaceutical advance: beta blockers for angina, the anxiolytics and antidepressants for psychiatric morbidity, preparations for common skin complaints such as dermatitis, and chemotherapy for gout provide examples in this context.

Consequently, a situation now exists in which the cost of the nation's drug bill is rising in order to accomodate these quality of life advances – the decade to 1981 saw an increase of 73 per cent in the real cost of pharmaceuticals to the NHS – but with only minimal compensatory growth in benefits of a strictly economic nature. And this situation requires attention if, particularly in the present economic and political climate in which resources for public service provision are tightly constrained, policy makers are to remain convinced of the value of new drug development. There is therefore a need to make more conspicuous the social benefits of medicine. Furthermore, in view of the nature of potential therapeutic advance this requirement will become more pressing over time.

Looking to the future, if it is accepted that man possesses an inbuilt biological clock ensuring that only very few will survive for more than 100 years, then a two fold health target would appear to confront society. The first objective is to raise the number of people who live a full lifespan. The second is to minimise the morbidity and disablement experienced during that life span. Combined, these goals are neatly encapsulated in Sir Richard Doll's expressed desire 'to die young as late as possible'.

Returning to the first objective, it is clear that much has still to be done in the context of reducing premature mortality. Figures for England and Wales reveal that there were nearly 580,000 deaths in 1981 and that more than 130,000 of these (that is 26 per cent) involved persons who had yet to celebrate their 65th birthday – a milestone still 5 and 10 years respectively short of current average life expectancies for males and females. Available evidence suggests, however, that the avoidance of a substantial proportion of these untimely deaths will depend upon behavioural change and more effective preventive medicine rather than pharmaceutical innovation. Behavioural or environmental factors are implicated, for example, in heart disease, lung cancer and accidental fatalities and these three groups currently account for almost half the deaths between the ages of 15 and 64.

This observation should not, however, be interpreted as a complete negation of any potential role whatsoever for pharmaceutical innovation in

C

the reduction of premature mortality. Research in the field of cancer – exploring new employment modes for existing chemotherapeutic agents, the role of interferon and vaccines – and directed at the vascular system – exploiting the growing understanding of the factors that influence the balance between thrombosis and unrestricted blood flow – will lead to some saving of life.

Generally speaking, however, it would be unrealistic to suppose that future developments in chemotherapy will influence premature mortality to a degree that will stand comparison with the impact of the anti-infective medicines of the First Pharmacological Revolution. Instead the fruits of the predicted new wave of drug development – or the Second Pharmacological Revolution – will benefit the second of the two targets noted earlier: disabling morbidity or the quality of life. Thus it is hoped that with sustained research initiatives effective therapeutic intervention will become available for diseases such as multiple sclerosis and rheumatoid arthritis. Neither of these are major causes of hospital admission, sickness absence from work or death (in 1980 the two diseases combined were responsible for less than 1,600 deaths or just 0.21 per cent of all mortality in that year). Yet both involve substantial personal and social costs for affected individuals because they generate impairments and handicaps which frequently have to be endured over prolonged periods of time.

Similarly, increasing understanding of the nature and functioning of neurotransmitters in mental and central nervous system disease might eventually yield an effective chemotherapeutic means of intervening in senile dementia. Such an advance would not only clearly generate substantial benefits for the 700,000 people over 65 years of age estimated to be suffering from this cause of mental deterioration but would also greatly improve the quality of life for the relatives and friends who have increasingly had to assume the burden of care created by the disease. Effective therapy might also be expected to release the hospital and other institutional resources absorbed in caring for individuals who do not have others to look after them in the community. Future therapeutic progress is unlikely, therefore, to remain entirely unaccompanied by benefits of an economic nature, but in general these will probably be of secondary significance to the expected social gains.

In conclusion, it cannot be claimed that OHE was the first to recognise that the use of medicines is accompanied by economic benefits. In 1959, three years before OHE was established, the report of the Hinchliffe Committee on the cost of prescribing drew attention to the fact that 'the community as a whole derives tremendous benefits from the growing use of the pharmaceutical service, not only in terms of relief of suffering and saving of life but also financially'. It can be argued, however, that OHE was among the leaders in subsequent attempts to quantify systematically these economic gains. Today twenty years later, in the contemporary transition from First to Second Revolution therapeutics, OHE has recognised a pressing need for the development of more appropriate methods of representing the benefits of new medicines. It has therefore taken the initiative by publishing this volume from which, it is hoped, will emerge a clearer understanding of the nature of the social benefits accompanying pharmaceutical therapy and the means by which they may be quantified.

The case of Tagamet

Alan Maynard
University of York

Introduction

The theme of this volume is the economic assessment of the social benefits of medicines. The themes of this paper are concerned with how the economics 'tool-kit' was applied to a pharmaceutical innovation, cimetidine (trade name: Tagamet), and how the results of this application could be improved. Thus my concern will be with the 'nuts and bolts' of the study by Tony Culyer and myself[1] and the ways in which this study could be elaborated and improved.

The objectives of the economist concerned with the evaluation of alternative ways of treating patients are to identify and quantify the costs and benefits of the alternative therapies and to present this information in a way which improves the quality of decision making. Economic evaluation is unlikely to generate definitive results: the more likely outcome is better information presented in a systematic and explicit framework. Hopefully better and more explicit information about alternative patterns of care will contribute to decisions which lead to the more efficient use of resources than would take place without economic evaluation.

The Economic Evaluation of Cimetidine

After a brief review of some aspects of the epidemiology of duodenal ulcer (DU) disease, the treatment options for DU patients will be outlined. The characteristics of an economic appraisal will then be presented and the contents of the Culyer-Maynard study will be outlined.

The epidemiology of DU-disease

In general the quantity and quality of epidemiological evidence about the prevalence (the stock at a given point in time) and incidence (flow or growth in the stock per period of time) of disease is very poor, The epidemiological data about DU disease are typical and pose the first problem for those interested in economic evaluation: many aspects of the economic evaluation will be tentative because of the poor epidemiological data base.

At the time of the Culyer-Maynard study the current view of the epidemiology of DU-disease was that summarised in Table 1.[2] The Table 1 data demonstrate that few studies of peptic ulcer disease* have been undertaken and that the prevalence estimates vary considerably.

Fry on the basis of the experience acquired in his general practice, estimated that about 16 per 1,000 patients present annually with symptoms severe enough to merit medical attention.[3] Fry takes a life-cycle view of the natural history of DU disease arguing that the typical DU episode is one of increasing disability, a peak and then remission. The average life of a

---

* A peptic ulcer is an erosion of a small part of the lining of the stomach (gastric ulcer) or the duodenum (duodenal ulcer), or occasionally of other parts of the digestive tract.

TABLE 1   **The prevalence of peptic ulcers**

Authors	Year	Population	Age group	Prevalence (per cent)
Knutsen and Selvaag	1947	Ration applicants (Norway)	20–59 (men)	4.2
Doll *et al*	1951	Occupational groups (England)	25 plus (men)	5.2
Fry	1964	GP list (England)	all ages (men)	6.6
Weir and Backett	1968	GP list (rural Scotland)	15 plus (men)	10.2
Clarke *et al*	1976	Random sample (Lambeth)	25–64 (men)	6.7

Source   Clarke *et al*, page 120 (Reference 2).

duodenal ulcer appears to be about five to 10 years with males typically having their onset in the 30 to 39 years age bracket with a peak after about eight years, and females experiencing a peak in intensity after about seven years with onset in the 40 to 49 years age bracket.

There is some evidence that the level of peptic ulcer disease in Britain and other societies has declined since the 1950s. Table 2 reproduces some evidence presented by Morris.[4] Further evidence of this trend can be found in Sussex[5] and Meade *et alia*.[6] The causes of this trend are unclear as is the exact cause of DU disease.

The epidemiology of the disease is also unclear and relatively few estimates of its prevalence and incidence are available. There seems to be agreement that there is a DU cycle with natural remission for the majority of patients. Only for the minority of patients is a radical intervention treatment in the form of surgery required: prior to cimetidine, figures of 15 to 20 per cent of patients were quoted as requiring surgery.[7]

Treatment options
Often the most difficult part of an evaluation is the identification of the treatment options and the selection of those options to be appraised. In the case of DU disease the following options appear relevant:
  i) do nothing (and await natural remission)
  ii) regulate diet and stress (a bland diet in a monastery will often lead to healing of the ulcer)
  iii) antacids
  iv) surgery (selective truncal or proximal vagotomy, a difficult technique to learn and a large number of cases needed on which to acquire and maintain skill)
  v) drug therapy (an H_2 antagonist such as cimetidine or rimetidine)
  vi) combinations of (i) to (v).

The introduction of cimetidine in the mid-1970s led to significant improvements in the quality of life for many DU patients. Walan reviews the many cimetidine trials performed over the world (Table 3) and shows that cimetidine effectively promotes healing of active duodenal ulcers.[8] The healing rate after 4–6 weeks treatment with cimetidine (mean 79 per cent,

TABLE 2 **Some historical trends in peptic ulcers: epidemiological measures of burden***

1 Mortality (Peptic Ulcers)

1922–4	9.1
1930–2	14.1
1940–2	19.2
1950–2	17.8
1960–2	9.2
1970–2	5.6

2 Admissions to Hospital

	Total for peptic ulcers	DU only Perforation	DU only Cold surgery	Haematesis and malaena for DU only
1956	478	55	126	—
1959	412	40	78	66
1962	428	32	105	70
1966	362	32	100	54
1972	299	—	—	—

3 Sickness Absence

	Spells of sickness	Days of incapacity
1954–5	450	30,000
1956–7	380	23,000
1966–7	340	19,000
1968–9	360	20,000
1970–1	300	15,000

* All data are annual rates per 100,000 for men aged 45–64

Source Morris (1975) page 17 (Reference 4).

range 60–92 per cent) is much greater than that after placebo (mean 38 per cent, range 19–60 per cent).

One of the general problems associated with these trials is that the nature of the placebo sometimes varies in quality or quantity. Also the trials reported to date are for short term use of the drug. For some patients the ulcer returns unless the cimetidine treatment is maintained. The effects of such treatment over decades is unknown but is now being assessed with long term trials. Critics of the drug fear that the reduced secretion of gastric acid induced by cimetidine may affect other stomach disease, in particular cancer. There seem to be no substantive evidence to substantiate these worries at present. Most trials of cimetidine compare its use with placebos or antacids. There has been little attempt to compare cimetidine with doing nothing or truncal vagotomy.

Cimetidine has been assessed in trials comparing its use with a placebo, or often an antacid regime. The results show significant differences and cimetidine, by healing duodenal ulcers, clearly improves the quality of life of many patients.

TABLE 3 Healing of duodenal ulcers. Endoscopically proven

Author	No of patients Cim	Plac	Healing (%) After 4 weeks Cim	Plac	After 6 weeks Cim	Plac
1 Albano et al (1978)	78	79	72	34		
2 Bank et al (1976)	19	19			86	42
3 Barakat et al (1979)	16	18	69	44		
4 Blackwood et al (1976)	21	21			62	19
5 Bodemar and Walan (1976)	30	14			90	36
6 Dobrilla et al (1978)	15	15	80	40		
7 Figueroa et al (1979)	13	16			92	43
8 Gilsanz et al (1979)	27	31			60*	45*
9 Gray et al (1979)	20	20	85	28		
10 Hentschel et al (1978)	44	47	73	32		
11 Hetzel et al (1978)	43	42			84	38
12 Mazure et al (1980)	17	19			82	50
13 Multicenter trial (1979)	134	46	66*	28*		
14 Semb et al (1977)	20	20	85	60		
15 Ubilluz et al	14	14	93	27		

*Healed ulcers and complete disappearance of erosions

Source Walan; Reference 8.

Evaluation: is the therapy worthwhile?

These clinical advantages over preceding therapies can only be gained at an opportunity cost. Thus the use of cimetidine consumes resources which, as a consequence, cannot be used to finance other health services which would advantage patients: to aid some patients, we have to deprive other patients of access to resources. As a consequence those interested in maximising the benefits derived from the use of scarce inputs must seek to answer the question is the therapy worth doing in relation to the alternative use of resources?

A variety of economic techniques can be used in an effort to answer such questions. Cost effectiveness analysis is concerned with the costs of alternative ways of achieving a given therapeutic end. Thus the outcomes are assumed to be identical, and the costs of the alternatives are analysed. Cost benefit analysis seeks to measure, in a common unit of account (money), the value of the costs and the outcomes of alternative methods of treating people.

The problem with cost effectiveness analysis is that the outcomes of the options are usually not identical. The problem with cost benefit analysis is that many of the outcomes (eg improved quality of life) are difficult to quantify, especially in monetary terms: clearly life after treatment with cimetidine is superior to life after surgery which removes part of the stomach and affects deleteriously diet and life style until death. The advantage of economic appraisal is that it provides an explicit framework in which to list and value where possible the 'hard' and 'soft' costs and benefits of the alternative therapies. Economic evaluation will not provide full information about the attributes of the options. It will provide an explicit set of estimates in a clear analytical framework.

Economic evaluation: worthwhile to whom?

If we seek to answer the question is the therapy worthwhile, confrontation of the question worthwhile to whom? is unavoidable. Some alternatives are:

i) is it worthwhile for the NHS? (if it is, which part of the NHS?) The risk is that the component parts of the public sector will 'shift' costs from themselves to others regardless of the efficient pattern of care.

ii) is it worthwhile for the patient?

iii) is it worthwhile for society?

The economist will argue that (iii) is the pertinent question: is it worthwhile for society? This approach obliges economists to identify the opportunity costs of alternative therapies to all the relevant decision makers in society eg:

i) the NHS

ii) local government and voluntary services

ii) all non-marketed inputs which care for the patients eg family time and the individual's time.

The evaluation of cimetidine

When Tony Culyer and I were confronted by the question of what type of study to carry out we considered some alternatives.

i) an economic and clinical appraisal following the random allocation of patients across a broad set of clinically relevant modes of care (see above). This has not been done.

ii) examine the effects of the introduction of a radical innovation such as cimetidine on clinical practice and use regression analyses ie detect the effects of cimetidine, 'other things being equal'. Work of this nature has been carried out by Weisbrod.[9]

iii) a longitudinal study to determine how patients move into and out of varying health states. This has not yet been done.

iv) a cost effectiveness study comparing the costs of surgery vis-a-vis cimetidine assuming initially that outcomes were the same. We attempted to do this.

Let us examine some problems of principle before describing the details of the study.

i   what is a cost?

There is a need to identify and value revenue (current) and capital costs.

This is very difficult as the basic NHS cost data are very poor. Average and total cost data are available but it is difficult to identify the crucial decision making variable ie the cost of treating one more patient (ie the marginal cost). Transfer payments (ie social security payments) are ignored because these represent changes in the ownership of shares of a given Gross National Product rather than changes in its size.

ii *discounting*

Adjusting for price changes separately (by using a deflator), it is also necessary to adjust for time preference. If we ask do you prefer £100 now or £100 in one year's time, you will usually prefer the benefits (£100) now. Conversely you will prefer to pay (costs) £100 in one year's time to £100 now. The rate at which you prefer benefits now (or costs next year) is called your time preference rate. There is argument about the precise rate to use (HM Treasury uses 7 per cent) but the calculation of costs over time periods requires discounting and sensitivity analysis to determine how the costs vary in response to alternative discount rates.

iii *are the benefits identical?*

Generally the quality of life with cimetidine appears to be superior to that of surgery. This is another 'plus' for cimetidine if it costs less. We did not have the time or resources to quantify this 'plus'.

In costing the surgical alternative we acquired hospital cost data from the Hospital Treasurer augmented with updated data from Hurst's study.[10] Using the poor epidemiological data, we identified and quantified the lost earnings associated with the alternatives arguing that this proxied the loss of production. It can be argued, in the 1980s, that the loss of production may be slight due to the availability of unemployed labour who can replace the DU patient in the labour force. Finally we identified the case fatality rate, taking a low estimate (0.5 per cent) compared to Hospital Inpatient Enquiry rate (5.6 per cent), and used it in relation to competing valuations of life to generate alternative estimates of the costs associated with death due to surgery.

The latter element of our study, the value of life or death avoidance, drew on the three alternative ways of valuing life (see Mooney; Reference 11):

i) the human capital approach: saving a life enables the beneficiary to earn and the value of this lifetime earnings pattern, suitably discounted, can be estimated (at a 7 per cent discount rate in 1978 this was £46,000).

ii) the social decisions approach: the value used by the Department of Transport per expected life saved from road and traffic improvements. The 1978 estimate of this loss of output, pain and grief, etc, was £68,500.

iii) the risk avoidance approach: the logic of this approach is to approach a population of 100 at risk. Suppose there is a procedure which reduces the risk of premature death for any one of them from 2 to 1 per cent ie if the procedure was used one premature death is avoided. Then acquire 100 individual valuations of the benefits of this risk reduction, sum these estimates and this is the value of life. Jones-Lee produces an estimate of £3 million by this method.[12]

The costs of this surgical alternative can then be compared to the costs of alternative drug regimes for 20, 25, 30 and 35 years duration at 5, 7 or 10 per cent discount rates.

We concluded that where the relevant treatment choice was surgery or cimetidine the lowest estimate of the surgical therapy (£1,080 at 1978 prices) was in excess of the lowest estimate of cimetidine (£1,010) and that the highest cimetidine cost (£1,240) was only slightly above the lowest surgical cost (£1,080) and well below that of the highest surgical cost (£16,370).

The deficiencies of this study are obvious:

i) it was an *ad hoc* study carried out after the innovation. It is much more sensible to involve the economist from the outset of the trials and collect economic data concurrently with clinical data: economic evaluation should take place whenever innovations induce significant resource consequences.

ii) we ignored the costs of alternatives in terms of their use of primary care. This procedure was adopted because of the lack of primary care data ie the high cost of acquiring relevant data. The effect of this is to reduce the cost of the cimetidine option. However we also ignored the resource consequences of primary care for surgery patients and we assume that this compensates for the omission of the primary care costs of the cimetidine option.

iii) it did not address the question of whether surgery contributed to reduced life expectation compared to the cimetidine option (again this omission makes the surgery option relatively more attractive).

iv) it did not address the question of for which patients is the surgery versus cimetidine choice relevant? Some surgeons argue that the introduction of cimetidine led to reduced surgery initially and then a 'bounce-back' as long term cimetidine treatment proved a poor alternative to surgery. This is an area of dispute. For some patients cimetidine and surgery may not be alternatives. For other patients there is the problem of the misapplication of the cimetidine therapy ie it may be often used inappropriately.

The Lessons from the Tagamet Case

Economic evaluation should be carried out alongside clinical evaluation. Failure to include economic elements in the design of clinical trials results in inappropriate data being collected and poor evaluation: retrospective economic evaluation is inefficient.

Another major group of problems arise from

i) the valuation of outputs. We used standard value of life techniques but ignored the quantification of the quality of life

ii) the selection of the discount rate

iii) the identification and valuation of 'hard' (eg NHS) and 'soft' (eg family) cost.

iv) estimates are crude and only remotely related to marginal costs

v) even if surgery is cheaper, do we save resources with the introduction of cimetidine? It is unlikely that we do as we cannot sack surgeons: they do other work. Thus output and costs rise.

What do you get for your efforts?
  i) the identification and discussion of alternatives in an explicit frame-work.
  ii) cost information about the alternatives
  iii) more information than now but does it improve decision making?
  iv) improved resource allocation will depend on incentives to use the information to direct action towards more efficient medical practice.

Systematic economic evaluation casts light on many consequences of choices in health care. Used rigorously it can improve decision making and lead to greater efficiency in the use of scarce resources.

REFERENCES

1 Culyer A J and Maynard A K (1981), The cost effectiveness of duodenal ulcer treatment, *Social Science and medicine*, vol 15C, No 1, p 3–11.
2 Clarke M, Halel T and Salmon N (1976), Peptic ulceration in men: epidemiology and medical care, *British Journal of Preventive and Social Medicine* 30, 115–122.
3 Fry J (1964), Peptic ulcer: a profile, *British Medical Journal* 2, 809.
4 Morris J N (1975), *Uses of Epidemiology*, 3rd edition, Churchill Livingston, London.
5 Susser A I (1967), Causes of peptic ulcer: a selective epidemiological review, *Journal of Chronic Disease*, 20, 435.
6 Meade T W, Arie T H and Brewis M *et alia* (1968), Recent history of schemic heart disease and duodenal ulcers in doctors, *British Medical Journal*, 3, 701.
7 Hallenbeck G A (1976), The natural history of duodenal ulcer disease, *Surgical Clinics of North America*, 56, 6, 1235–1242.
8 Walan A (1983), Clinical evaluation of cimetidine with special reference to socioeconomic effects, in A J Culyer and B Horisberger (eds), *The Economic Evaluation of Medical Technology*, Smith Kline Corporation.
9 Weisbrod B and Gwerke J (1981), Some economic consequences of technological advance in medical care: the case of a new drug in R B Helms (ed), *Drugs and Health*, American Enterprise Institute, Washington DC.
10 Hurst J W (1977), *Saving Hospital Expenditure by Reducing Inpatient Stay*, HM Treasury Government Economic Service, paper 14, HMSO.
11 Mooney G H (1976), *The Valuation of Human Life*, Macmillan, London.
12 Jones-Lee M W (1976), *The Value of Life: An Economic Analysis*, Martin Robertson, London.

The economics of heart transplant programmes: measuring the benefits

Martin Buxton
Brunel University

I Introduction to the research study

At the end of October 1981 DHSS research funds were granted to the Department of Economics at Brunel University and the Department of Community Medicine at the University of Cambridge to carry out, over a three-year period, co-ordinated studies of the costs and benefits of the cardiac transplantation programmes at Harefield and Papworth Hospitals. The research aims to identify and carry out a detailed analysis of the resource requirements, and thus the costs, of the current heart transplantation programmes at Papworth and Harefield Hospitals and to relate these to appropriate indicators of patient benefits. The study has three main elements:

1) the analysis of resource costs within Papworth and Harefield Hospitals associated with their respective transplantation programmes;
2) the identification and analysis of extra NHS costs and other public sector costs incurred outside the two centres by patients involved in the transplantation programmes and their selection procedures;
3) the measurement of benefits in terms of basic outcome data.

Thus the measurement of benefits is an integral part of the prospective study but in no way the sole focus of attention. Much of our research activity is related to identifying, measuring and costing the resources devoted to the transplant programmes. Whilst the costing side of the study raises many interesting issues this paper concentrates entirely on benefit measurement.

II Comparison groups

However, before discussing benefit measurement, it is important to focus on a fundamental problem in this study, as in many others, namely the difficulty of establishing a point of comparison. The study aims to consider the extra costs and benefits that stem from the existence of a transplant programme as compared with conventional management. However, the programmes were not set up in a formal experimental manner with a randomised control group. Indeed in the formal sense, not even a non-randomised control group exists against which to compare the costs and benefits of the transplanted patients. In the absence of such formal controls the study has to obtain as much relevant comparative information as is possible from the various patient groups accessible to the researchers. Figure 1 presents a basic decision tree diagram representing the possible outcomes for any patients within the relevant total population of heart disease, and thus defines the major patient sub-groups relevant to this study. The letters of the branches of this diagram are used as reference points to the particular patient groups in the text below.

Of the total population with heart disease of the types that might in some instances be treated by transplantation (U) some will be referred to either centre (A). The others who are not referred (B) will be unidentified and totally unknown to the research team. Of those who are referred, some may be considered unsuitable on the basis of established selection criteria and may therefore not be called for assessment (D). There seems to be few of these at Harefield and a declining number at Papworth. In practical terms, though identifiable, they are not a group that is easily accessible to the researchers.

Therefore for practical purposes the population we can 'monitor' is the assessment population (C), and we are attempting to collect information on all patients in this group. Once a decision has been made after assessment, this group is split into two – (E) accepted for transplant and (F) not accepted for transplant. At any point in time those accepted (who are still alive) are either transplanted (G) or waiting (H). Those not accepted may have had, as a result of the assessment, an alternative operation (I), or will have returned to their previous medical regime (J). Information on each of these four groups (G, H, I and J) will be available for comparative purposes.

In considering the benefits of transplantation, we require ideally a true control group of patients who are clinically strictly comparable to those accepted for transplant, but who are randomly allocated to continuing medical therapy. In the absence of such a control, a sub-group within (J)

FIGURE I **Basic decision tree diagram for a cardiac transplantation programme**

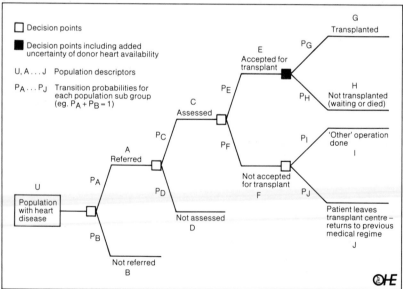

* The decision tree approach is consistent as an analysis of a point in time.

† The only problem is Group (H). Clearly those not transplanted at a point in time will include those in the transient state of still waiting for transplant.

such as those rejected on purely psychosocial grounds or because they were just outside the age limits, might come closest to meeting this criterion; in practice it seems such a sub-group would be very small indeed. As a whole (J) includes patients who are very different from those in (G). Moreover they are for obvious reasons the group of assessed patients with the weakest clinical links with the transplant centre, and hence possibly the most difficult group to monitor for this study.

Thus the main group against which comparisons can be made is group (H). Even this is not without problems in that the patients who die from that group *may* tend to be the iller patients for whom a suitable donor heart is not offered in time. The patients still waiting at any point in time *may* tend to be those with the relatively better prognosis who have not been put at the top of the 'waiting list'.

Thus any comparisons between these sub-groups have to be made with extreme caution and all reasons for differences between them will have to be fully explored in detailed analysis. Nevertheless only by obtaining information on these various comparison groups will it be possible to estimate the 'extra' benefits from transplantation as compared with existing 'routine' management.

III Benefit measures

Not unnaturally, heart transplant programmes tend to be viewed in the first instance in terms of their capacity for extending the length of patients' lives. The programmes are seen in terms of offering a 'new lease of life' to very ill patients for whom the prognosis is extremely poor.

The press coverage amd media comment has tended to be rather partial in its perspective, at times highlighting the dramatic changes in health of some fortunate transplant patients whilst at other times critically commenting on the programmes in terms of crude estimates of their short-term survival rates.

Whilst it is relatively easy to record survival statistics from the time of transplant or from the point of acceptance onto the programme, it is extremely difficult to devise a suitable statistical technique for establishing, in the absence of a RCT, the extent to which survival is increased by transplantation.

There is a considerable statistical literature on techniques for calculating comparative survival curves (from the point of acceptance) for the two subgroups of those accepted onto a transplant programme (i) who do receive transplants and (ii) who do not. The main problem in comparing these survival rates stems from the question whether the factors that determine which accepted patient receives a transplant can be deemed to be 'random' or whether they are 'biased'. The choice of recipient is inevitably restricted to those patients who have been well enough to survive until the point of time when the donor-heart becomes available: others may have died waiting. But the choice may be conversely 'biased' as a positive clinical decision towards the sickest of the remaining eligible patients.

Important though this issue is in the context of the research as a whole, I would like here to focus on the other aspect of benefit that we are attempting to measure. Survival and changes in length of life are but part of the expected output or benefits from cardiac transplantation. Changes in 'quality of life' are also to be expected. English, Cory-Pearce and McGregor note that, 'the quality of life of the 14 survivors' who at the time of writing had been discharged from Papworth Hospital 'has greatly improved, and most of the heart recipients are delighted with the degree of rehabilitation they have attained'.[1] Similarly a report of the Stanford experience stresses the importance of the quality of life of surviving recipients, focusing particularly on rehabilitation 'defined simply as restoration of overall functional capacity sufficient to provide the patient with an unrestricted option to return to active employment or an activity of choice'.[2]

Other studies have concentrated on the impact on the patients' families, in particular developing the work of Simmons at the University of Minnesota in the context of renal transplantation.[3] Currently the National Heart Transplantation Study in the USA (funded by the Office of Research and Demonstrations of the Health Care Financing Administration, Department of Health and Human Services) is developing a detailed questionnaire for use with the families of transplant patients focusing particularly on the effects of the operation on family relationships.[4]

Whilst recognising the importance of both return to active work and the impact on the family as measures of particular aspects of quality of life, the research team were concerned to adopt an existing well validated instrument as a basic measure that would provide a more general indicator of the patients' health status.

Apart from the usual constraints of available research resources, two related factors limited our scope in deciding how to measure benefits. Firstly, there was a pressing need to ensure that the methodology for measuring benefits that we adopted could be put into operation within a very short period after the start of the study. The research protocol had clearly recognised the uncertainty about the continued funding of the two transplant programmes. [The funding was, at that stage, only assured until the end of December 1982 (at Papworth) and the end of March 1983 (at Harefield).] Secondly, the programmes were expected to involve a fairly small number of actual transplant cases (in the order of 15–20 transplants per year at each centre). For both these reasons it was vital that we minimised any delay in beginning to measure the 'quality of life' of patients before and after transplant.

But in search of an appropriate instrument we were once again struck by a grave imbalance between the massive volume of literature stressing the importance of using health status measures in evaluative research, and the handful of even partially acceptable developed instruments for such measurement. In 1976 Bergner *et al* suggested that, 'from the perspective of those assigned the task of evaluating health programmes, the greatest impediments to effective evaluation are the lack of professional consensus as to what constitutes an appropriate outcome measure and the concern that cultural differences among individuals and groups may yield problematic results when a single measure is used with a diverse population'.[5] It is still a major impediment, although certain instruments do now exist.

It is not the purpose of this paper to attempt a systematic review of the literature, particularly the vast number of conceptual and theoretical papers on health status/quality of life measurement. Many useful surveys already exist.[6–9] However, it may be relevant to subsequent discussions to describe briefly the various instruments we considered, and to indicate how we viewed their strengths and weaknesses from the point of view of our particular needs.

The literature identifies three broad conceptions of health on which individuals base their appraisal of their own health status – feeling-state, clinical, and performance.[10] In that our primary concern was to collect information on the health states of patients as they perceived their own health, and independently of clinical judgement, we obviously wished to avoid any approach that relied on clinical assessments or indeed any other external interpretation of health states. This effectively restricted us to feeling-state or performance conceptions.

The nature of the evaluative context of this study and resource and time constraints further limited our choice. Apart from the obvious questions of methodological soundness and empirical validity, we identified the following criteria for a subjective health measure appropriate to this study:

(a) any measure had to be sensitive to a wide range of health states, and appropriate to patients both before and after transplant;

(b) the process of assessment had to be acceptable to patients, and any questions easily and unambiguously understood;

(c) preferably, it should be possible to elicit the necessary information by post, rather than merely by direct interview;

(d) the measure should have been used, or should be likely to be used, in studies of other relevant comparison groups;

(e) a minimum of developmental work should be required so that the method could be commenced as quickly as possible, and the system of collection and analysis of the data should be consistent with our available resources.

It was clear that criteria (d) and (e) required that we should, if at all possible, adopt an existing validated and widely used research instrument. We recognised that we had neither the time, nor the particular expertise, to construct a new instrument. Indeed our concern for comparability with other studies emphasised that we should avoid making any changes to an existing instrument.

IV The available instruments
The following instruments were seen as deserving our formal consideration as a basic element of our measurement of health status.

A *Guttman scales related to physical dependency*
Guttman scaling techniques applied to data on physical dependency (in terms of performance of activities of everyday living) have now been used in several recent studies.[11, 12] It has proved a very effective method for considering groups where differing degrees of physical disability are of primary concern and other aspects of health of relative unimportance. To extend the approach to multi-dimensional scaling is much more complex and less well tried. We were concerned that (a) physical dependence was not a sufficiently broad basis for measuring the expected changes; (b) a Guttman Physical Dependency Scale was unlikely to offer a sufficiently fine indicator

of change, and (c) its use on relevant comparison groups had not occurred and would not necessarily do so.

B *Government social survey classification*

This potentially offered a fully developed and tested instrument which had in particular been used in the study of 'Handicapped and Impaired in Great Britain'.[13] It focuses on performance of living activities and classifies people into categories reflecting degrees of handicap based on ability for self-care. Whilst this is a very fully tested classification it was seen as (a) too narrow for our purposes (one of the main purposes of the Harris enquiry was to estimate the number of people whose capacity for self-care was limited to the extent that they might qualify for an attendance allowance), and (b) reliant on a very complex direct interview.

C *'Wessex' questionnaires*

Researchers in Wessex devised a specific set of questionnaires to address the question of quality of life after open-heart surgery, and information was elicited on physical activity, employment, dependence on others, leisure activities, mood and sexual relationships.[14] The questionnaire had the appeal that the aspects of life under question were those apparently most relevant to cardiac patients. Additionally the patients covered in the original survey would have formed an interesting comparison group for our own study. However, we had serious reservations about the construct of certain aspects of the questionnaire. Many of the questions, although interesting in their own right, produced substantive information which could not easily be incorporated into a summary health-status index or profile. Additionally the specificity of the selection of questions to cardiac problems (whilst an apparent advantage in itself) makes it very unlikely that it will be used in studies of non-cardiac patients. Thus we would not be able to put any results we obtained into context by comparing them with other unrelated patient groups. Certainly no general population norms are available for comparison.

D *Index of well-being*

This stems from the ambitious attempt to construct a totally validated index of well-being, 'that aggregates different outcomes, including death, from many different health problems on a single scale'.[15] Whilst this approach has been widely reported in the literature, it is effectively still at a developmental stage, and there is, as far as we are aware, no UK experience even of its experimental use. Despite the considerable merit for a study of this sort, of having a single index of general well-being, its use was not a practical possibility.

E *Functional limitations profile (FLP)*

Contemporaneous work in the University of Washington, Seattle, has produced an instrument that could be utilised at this stage.[5, 16] The Sickness Impact Profile (SIP) is a, 'behaviourally based measure of the impact of sickness'. It uses a set of statements, 'which must (a) describe the behaviour and (b) specify the nature of the dysfunction. Dysfunction was defined as including modification or impairment in degree or manner of carrying out an activity, cessation of an activity, or initiation of a new activity that interferes with or substitutes for a usual activity.' These statements are then grouped under various headings such as, social interaction, sleep and rest activity, usual daily work, household management, mobility, etc. For each statement in the SIP, respondents are asked to state whether it describes them 'today' and, if so, whether it is due to their health. If the answer is yes to both parts of the question that aspect of limitation is recorded and, using socially derived weights for the severity of various statements within each category, a score for that category is calculated. A total score can be calculated by simple aggregation of the category scores. The SIP has been very thoroughly developed and validated in the USA.

Moreover, it has now been adapted for use in England by Patrick.[17] He has both translated the behavioural statements, 'to conform to British English', whilst attempting to retain full comparability with the American version, and has calculated local weights reflecting local social preferences and views about the relative severity of the various limitations/dysfunctional characteristics.

Patrick's version of SIP, which he calls the Functional Limitation Profile (FLP) has been used in his study of the Physically Handicapped in Lambeth.[18, 19] It consists of 136 statements grouped into twelve categories: eating; body care and movement; ambulation; mobility; usual daily work; household management; recreation and pastimes; sleep and rest; communication; alertness behaviour; emotional behaviour, and social interaction. It is intended for use in an interview.

F   *Nottingham health profile (NHP)*
This health profile, devised by a team from the department of Community Medicine at Nottingham University School of Medicine adopts a very similar approach to the FLP. It similarly sets out to measure subjective health status through asking for responses to a carefully selected set of 38 simple statements relating to six areas of social functioning: pain; energy; physical mobility; sleep; social isolation, and emotional reactions.

The actual statements in each section are given in Figure 2. Patients are required simply to answer yes or no to each statement, 'according to whether the statement applies to him or her in general at the time of completing the profile'. All statements relate to limitations on activity, etc. 'Full health' is thus defined as the absence of any of these limitations and scores zero in each section. The weights enable a score from 0–100 to be calculated for each section of the profile in discrete steps depending upon the number and weights of statements within that section. Scores of 100 in any section indicate that the respondent suffers from all the limitations included in that section of the NHP. The process by which these statements were derived and chosen, and the system of weights to be applied to them, are presented in detail elsewhere,[20, 22] and in the paper in this volume by Dr J. McEwen – one of the principal researchers involved in its development. A recent study has however shown how crucially the values of the weights depend upon the scaling model used and suggests that for at least one category (sleep) alternative weights are equally compatible with the original data from which the weights were derived.[23]

The economics of heart transplant programmes: measuring the benefits 41

FIGURE 2 **Nottingham health profile: listing of statements**

Physical mobility
I find it hard to reach for things
I find it hard to bend
I have trouble getting up and down stairs or
    steps
I find it hard to stand for long (eg, at the
    kitchen sink, waiting for a bus)
I can only walk about indoors
I find it hard to dress myself
I need help to walk about outside (eg, a
    walking aid or someone to support me)
I'm unable to walk at all

Pain
I'm in pain when going up and down stairs
    or steps
I'm in pain when I'm standing
I find it painful to change position
I'm in pain when I'm sitting
I'm in pain when I walk
I have pain at night
I have unbearable pain
I'm in constant pain

Sleep
I'm waking up in the early hours of the
    morning
It takes me a long time to get to sleep

I sleep badly at night
I take tablets to help me sleep
I lie awake for most of the night

Energy
I soon run out of energy
Everything is an effort
I am tired all the time

Social isolation
I'm finding it hard to get on with people
I'm finding it hard to make contact with
    people
I feel there is nobody I am close to
I feel lonely
I feel I am a burden to people

Emotional reactions
The days seem to drag
I'm feeling on edge
I have forgotten what it is like to enjoy
    myself
I lose my temper easily these days
Things are getting me down
I wake up feeling depressed
Worry is keeping me awake at night
I feel as if I'm losing control
I feel that life is not worth living

The devisers of the Profile stress that the scores from the different sections should not be aggregated to give an overall score but that the scores
should be presented as a 'profile'.

Part II of the NHP relates to, 'those areas of "task performance" most
affected by health'. In the final version, Part II consists of seven statements
referring to the effects of health problems on: occupation; ability to perform tasks around the home; personal relationships; sex life; social life;
hobbies and holidays. In this section respondents are asked to answer 'yes'
to any of the activities if their present state of health is causing problems
and affecting them. No weights have been calculated for Part II and a
simple count of the affirmative responses is used as a summary statistic for
Part II.

The NHP was devised from the outset as a questionnaire that could easily
be administered by post. It has been applied to a fairly wide range of
groups, all or most of which provide interesting comparisons to put the
scores observed in this study into context.

V Our choice of instrument

Both the Harris/Government Social Survey Classification and any specific Guttman scale for physical disability seemed far too narrow for our purposes. We were concerned that we should be able to identify major changes in other aspects of health including emotional changes.

Whilst the Wessex questionnaires had considerable merit because of their specific focus on aspects of health likely to be affected by cardiac problems, this very same specificity means that they cannot be seen as producing measures of health state (or illness state) as a whole. Any results would be difficult (if not impossible) to compare with results from other groups of patients suffering from other illnesses or with 'norms' for a general population. In addition we had strong reservations about the underlying methodology and analytical theory.

The choice between the FLP and NHP was much more difficult. In theory by eliciting answers to a greater number of statements the FLP should be a more sensitive indicator of subjective health state, and less likely to be over sensitive to the answer to any single statement. However in practice, the greater number of statements is not a wholly beneficial factor: there are whole categories of functional limitations each with their several questions that may seem irrelevant to the respondent. We saw its sheer length as a potential problem, particularly if it were used by post rather than in the intended interview situation. Given the desire to be able to use the questionnaire on a self-administered postal basis, these reservations led us to doubts about the level of compliance we might expect if we adopted the FLP. We feared that we might experience both a higher level of non-response and a greater degree of misinterpretation than with the simpler and shorter NHP.

We did consider using particularly relevant parts (ie, specific sections) of the FLP in addition to the NHP, but after some initial experimentation rapidly dropped the idea because of the rather different requirements of the two questionnaires as regards the patient's interpretation and completion of the questions and the fear that there might well be confusion.

It was decided that, given the NHP was suitable for postal use, we would basically aim to have it completed by patients at three-monthly intervals. It would be administered by one of the researchers as part of a fuller interview at initial assessment at Papworth or Harefield, and at any subsequent assessment or pre-operative admission irrespective of the elapsed time. For any patients 'waiting' for transplants the questionnaire would be repeated on a postal basis at three-monthly intervals. Thus whenever a transplant operation takes place the recipient should have completed a questionnaire not more than three months earlier and, probably, more recently than that.

The initial decision was to have NHP's completed at six weeks, and at three months, and then at three-monthly intervals after transplant. The six-week profile has however now been dropped in that the patient (often still hospitalised) frequently found the profile difficult to complete in that the opportunity had not arisen to attempt (or to need to undertake) certain of the activities.

The same three-monthly pattern applies to all patients assessed (for as long as we can obtain their co-operation).

VI   The use of the Profile scores

In this study, the most powerful use of the NHP will come from observing the individual patient's score at assessment (and at any other pre-operative administration of the Profile) and comparing this (these) with post operative scores over a period of time. Such individual longitudinal comparisons can then be aggregated to compare average change over time for groups of patients, and within the limits of the total numbers of cases some attempts can be made to look for factors relating to different degrees of change (age, medical condition, etc).

At this stage, our full analysis of these data has not commenced. Indeed we have available only a small number of pre-transplant and three months post-transplant observations from each centre reflecting the small numbers who have been assessed *and* transplanted since April 1982 when we were able to begin routinely to use the NHP. Eleven pairs of profile scores of the same patients including patients from the Harefield and Papworth programmes are presented in Table 1.

For these small numbers of paired comparisons with a large proportion of zero scores, we have followed the methodology recommended by the devisers of the NHP and used the Wilcoxon matched-pairs signed rank test of significance of differences in each elements of Part I of the profile.[24]

It will be noted that in only five instances did patient scores 'deteriorate' and no patients showed a deterioration on more than one aspect of the Profile. Indeed, only for the aspect of sleep did more than one patient record a deterioration. In many cases dramatic improvements occurred, particularly in relation to improvements in energy and physical mobility. It is not surprising therefore to find as shown in Table 2 that for all aspects of Part I of the Profile, the post-transplant scores represent a statistically significant improvement in 'health'.

TABLE 1   **Nottingham health profile: paired comparisons pre-transplant and three-month post-transplant patient profile scores**
Illustrative pooled data from the Harefield and Papworth programmes

Patient No	Pre-op score x_1	Post-op score x_2	Difference $d = x_2 - x_1$	Rank of absolute difference $[d]$	Signed rank +	Signed rank −
Physical Mobility						
1	54.89	0	−54.89	9		9
2	58.20	21.99	−36.21	4		4
3	78.70	19.87	−58.83	10		10
4	45.25	0	−45.25	8		8
5	41.86	0	−41.86	5		5
6	55.98	11.77	−44.21	7		7
7	43.98	0	−43.98	6		6
8	21.99	0	−21.99	2		2
9	31.36	0	−31.36	3		3
10	21.36	0	−21.36	1		1
11	78.70	0	−78.70	11		11
			(n=11)	Rank sums:	0	66

Patient No	Pre-op score x_1	Post-op score x_2	Difference $d = x_2 - x_1$	Rank of absolute difference [d]	Signed rank +	Signed rank −
Pain						
1	66.23	0	−66.23	9		9
2	0	0	0	—		—
3	24.13	9.99	−14.14	3		3
4	36.79	0	−36.79	7		7
5	100.00	44.26	−55.74	8		8
6	0	10.49	+10.49	2	2	
7	29.96	0	−29.96	6		6
8	0	0	0	—		—
9	17.05	0	−17.05	4.5		4.5
10	17.05	0	−17.05	4.5		4.5
11	9.99	0	−9.99	1		1
			(n=9)	Rank sums:	2	43
Sleep						
1	16.10	34.27	+18.17	1	1	
2	100.00	0	−100.00	9		9
3	77.63	12.57	−65.06	8		8
4	0	0	0	—		—
5	100.00	72.74	−27.26	6		6
6	77.63	77.63	0	—		—
7	34.94	12.57	−22.37	3.5		3.5
8	22.37	0	−22.37	3.5		3.5
9	34.94	0	−34.94	7		7
10	0	22.37	+22.37	3.5	3.5	
11	22.37	0	−22.37	3.5		3.5
			(n=9)	Rank sums:	4.5	40.5
Energy						
1	100.00	0	−100.00	8.5		8.5
2	100.00	24.00	−76.00	6		6
3	100.00	0	−100.00	8.5		8.5
4	100.00	0	−100.00	8.5		8.5
5	24.00	0	−24.00	2		2
6	24.00	24.00	0	—		—
7	60.80	0	−60.80	4.5		4.5
8	24.00	0	−24.00	2		2
9	60.80	0	−60.80	4.5		4.5
10	24.00	0	−24.00	2		2
11	100.00	0	−100.00	8.5		8.5
			(n=10)	Rank sums:	0	55
Social Isolation						
1	41.89	19.36	−22.53	3.5		3.5
2	57.86	0	−57.86	7		7
3	22.53	41.89	+19.36	1	1	
4	22.53	0	−22.53	3.5		3.5
5	0	0	0	—		—
6	0	0	0	—		—
7	22.53	0	−22.53	3.5		3.5
8	44.54	0	−44.54	6		6
9	22.53	0	−22.53	3.5		3.5
10	0	0	0	—		—
11	0	0	0	—		—
			(n=7)	Rank sums:	1	27

Patient No	Pre-op score x_1	Post-op score x_2	Difference $d = x_2 - x_1$	Rank of absolute difference [d]	Signed rank +	Signed rank −
Emotional Reactions						
1	51.55	38.05	−13.50	4		4
2	73.29	0	−73.29	11		11
3	62.47	0	−62.47	10		10
4	21.17	0	−21.17	6		6
5	27.31	0	−27.31	8		8
6	16.84	0	−16.84	5		5
7	9.31	9.76	+0.45	1	1	
8	39.01	0	−39.01	9		9
9	7.08	0	−7.08	2.5		2.5
10	7.08	0	−7.08	2.5		2.5
11	27.00	0	−27.00	7		7
		(n=11)		Rank sums:	1	65

Obviously these changes need to be considered in the context of data that are beginning to emerge of the longer-term health state of these patients. Similarly the results need to be compared with changes over time for those who did not receive transplants. Additionally as more data become available, it will become feasible to present separate analyses relating to each programme, and to particular sub-groups of patients.

Reservations can of course be raised about the validity of such scores. Most importantly perhaps is the question of whether post-transplant 'euphoria' and simple gratitude for having received a transplant, leads patients to misrepresent their health state (consciously or subconsciously). In practice we believe that the patients' subject NHP scores seem to tally well with the informal expectations and views of both the researchers involved and the clinicians concerned. At this stage it is not reasonable to claim more than that the NHP appears to be producing satisfactory results. Combined with other more impressionistic data from detailed semi-structured interviews that we are carrying out with the patients, it seems to offer the most appropriate available instrument for measuring subjective health states in this particular study.

TABLE 2 **Nottingham health profile: paired comparisons pre-transplant and three-month post-transplant patient profile scores Statistical significance of differences (presented in Table I)**

	Number of ranked differences	Wilcoxon T statistic	Level at which difference is significant
Physical Mobility	11	0	0.01
Pain	9	2	0.02
Sleep	9	4.5	0.05
Energy	10	0	0.01
Social Isolation	7	1	0.05
Emotional Reactions	11	1	0.01

VII Relating quantity and quality of life

The NHP does not of course come close to an economist's theoretical ideal, Unfortunately, it gives just what its name suggests – a Profile indicating scores under its six main (Part I) headings. It is a multi-dimensional measure of 'quality of life', not a unidimensional index. It is interesting to speculate why McEwen and colleagues in constructing the NHP failed to make the step to a system for weighting the parts of the profile into a single score whilst Patrick and colleagues made that useful (but heroic) step. The difficulties of establishing individual trade-offs between different aspects of health (eg, pain and immobility) have been frequently discussed in the literature for many years,[25, 26] and are discussed at greater length in other papers in this volume.

But even if these problems are overcome and some of our reservations about making interpersonal comparisons are withheld, and we so achieve a unidimensional qualitative measure of health status, there is still the major question of how to relate such a measure of quality to measures of quantity of life. The upper and lower limits of the scores as produced by the NHP are arbitrary. Whilst we may well be prepared to ignore the all-embracing World Health Organisation's definition of health and accept as a working premise that a zero score on all aspects of the NHP can be considered as an adequate proxy for 'full health', it is aboslutely clear that a score of 100 on all aspects of the NHP does not represent zero health (certainly if zero health is presumed to be equivalent to death). It is a problem in general, that such scores involve an arbitrary location of the maximum (poorest health-state) score on the continuum between full-health and death and do not differentiate between various degrees of extreme absence of health. This, of course, is a significant problem observed in this study. On particular aspects of Part I of the NHP many pre-transplant patients score 100, and post-transplant many score 0. In each case the arbitrary limit hides variations in health state.

Ideally in this study, as in so many others, we would have liked a single index reflecting trade-offs of all the various dimensions of 'quality of life', cardinally calibrated to cover the whole spectrum of illness to an acceptable definition of 'zero' quality of life. Then it might be possible to establish individuals' trade-offs between quantity and quality and move towards a single index of health service output encompassing both these dimensions.

The concept of 'quality adjusted life years' has enormous intuitive appeal. It has been mooted in the literature for many years and indeed was used in 1968 to differentiate the quality of life under renal dialysis and after renal transplant in Klarmann's pioneering cost-effectiveness study.[27] However in that case, the quality 'weighting' was an arbitrary judgement of the researchers. More recently, McNeil, Weichselbaum and Pauker attempted to identify empirically individual trade-offs between alternative treatments for laryngeal cancer, which offer different prospects of survival allied to different qualities of life.[28] (In this rather limited case only two qualitative states – with or without speech impairment – were considered, but nevertheless interesting information on patient trade-offs between mortality and morbidity were elicited.)

Unfortunately, empirical progress with measures of health state has lagged far behind the theory. Despite the frequent restatements of the importance of such a scale for health service evaluation studies, applied research still lacks an empirically validated scale that offers a practical basis for explicitly bringing together quantity and quality in a generally acceptable way. The relevant research community must attempt to define, fund and co-ordinate a campaign of research to move us actively towards this Holy Grail, assuming that this theoretical ideal is in fact attainable. In the meantime empirical research must make intelligent use of the limited instruments currently available, to begin systematically to measure the quantitative and qualitative dimensions of the benefits of health service interventions.

REFERENCES

1 English T A H, Cory-Pearce R, and McGregor C. 'Heart Transplantation at Papworth Hospital' *Heart Transplantation* vol 1, no 2, 1982, pp 110–111.

2 Pennock J L, *et al.* 'Cardiac Transplantation in Perspective for the Future: Survival, Complications, Rehabilitation, and Cost' *Journal of Thoracic and Cardiovascular Surgery* vol 83, 1982, pp 168–177.

3 Simmons R G, Klein S D, and Simmons R L. *Gift of Life: The Social and Psychological Impact of Organ Transplantation* New York: Wiley Inter Science, 1977.

4 Evans R W. *Dimensions of Family Impact Pertinent to Heart Transplantation* National Heart Transplantation Study: Update no 8, June 1982, (mimeo).

5 Bergner M, *et al.* 'The Sickness Impact Profile: Conceptual Formulation and Methodology for the Development of a Health Status Measure' *International Journal of Health Services* vol 6, no 3, 1976, pp 393–415.

6 Culyer A, Lavers A, and Williams A. 'Social Indicators: Health', *Social Trends* vol 2, 1971, pp 31–42.

7 Sackett D L, *et al.* 'The Development and Application of Indices of Health: General Methods and a Summary of Results', *American Journal of Public Health* vol 67, 1977, pp 423–428.

8 Williams R G A. 'Theories and Measurement in Disability', *Journal of Epidemiology and Community Medicine* vol 33, 1979, pp 32–44.

9 Williams A. 'Welfare Economics and Health Status Measurement' in van der Gaag J and Perlman M (eds) *Health, Economics, and Health Economics* Amsterdam, North Holland, 1981.

10 Baumann B. 'Diversities in Conceptions of Health and Physical Fitness' *Journal of Health and Human Behaviour* vol 2, no 1, 1961, pp 39–46.

11 Williams R G A, *et al.* 'Disability: a Model and Measurement Technique' *British Journal Of Preventive and Social Medicine* vol 30, 1976, pp 71–78.

12 Wright K G, Cairns J A, and Snell M C. *Costing Care* University of Sheffield Joint Unit for Social Services Research Monograph: Research in Practice, Sheffield, 1981.

13 Harris A I. *Handicapped and Impaired in Great Britain: Part I* Office of Population, Censuses and Surveys: Social Survey Division, HMSO, London, 1971.

14 Ross J K, *et al.* 'The Quality of Life After Cardiac Surgery' *British Medical Journal* 7 February 1981, pp 451–453.

15 Bush J W, Blischke W R, and Berry C C. 'Health Indices, Outcomes and the Quality of Medical Care' in Yaffe R and Zalkind D (eds) *Evaluation in Health Services Delivery* New York, Engineering Foundation, 1975, pp 313–339.

16 Bergner M, *et al.* 'The Sickness Impact Profile: Validation of a Health Status Measure' *Medical Care* vol XIV, no 1, 1976, pp 57–67.

17 Patrick D. 'Standardization of Comparative Health Status Measures: Using Scales Developed in America in an English Speaking Country' in *Proceedings of the Third Biennial Conference on Health Survey Research Methods* (Reston, Va; 17th May 1980), published by National Centre for Health Services Research, US DHSS, Publication no PHS 81–3268, 1980, pp 216–220.

18 Patrick D (ed). *The Longitudinal Disability Interview Survey: Phase I Report* Social Medicine and Health Services Research Unit, St Thomas's Hosptial Medical School, 1981, London.

19 Patrick D (ed). *The Longitudinal Disability Interview Survey: Phase II Report* Social Medicine and Health Services Research Unit, St Thomas's Hospital Medical School, 1982, London.

20 Backett E M, McEwen J, and Hunt S M. *Health and Quality of Life: End of Grant Report to SSRC* HR 6157/1, 1981, (mimeo).

21 Hunt S M, KcKenna S P, and McEwen J. *The Nottingham Health Profile: Manual* 1982, (mimeo).

22 KcKenna I W, Hunt S M, and McEwen J. 'Weighting the Seriousness of Perceived Health Problems using Thurstone's Method of Paired Comparisons', *International Journal of Epidemiology* vol 10, no 1, 1981, pp 93–97.

23 Kind P. 'A Comparison of Two Models for Scaling Health Indicators' *International Journal of Epidemiology* vol 11, no 3, 1982, pp 271–275.

24 Hamburg M. *Statistical Analysis For Decision Making* 2nd Edition, Harcourt Brace Jovanovich, New York, 1977.

25 Williams A. 'Measuring the Effectiveness of Health Care Systems' *British Journal of Preventive and Social Medicine* vol 28, 1974, pp 196–202.

26 Rosser R, and Watts V. 'The Measurement of Hospital Output', *International Journal of Epidemiology* vol 1, 1972.

27 Klarmann H F, Francis J O'S, and Rosenthal G D. 'Cost Effectiveness Analysis Applied to the Treatment of Chronic Renal Disease', *Medical Care* vol 6, 1968, pp 48–54.

28 McNeil B J, Weichselbaum R, and Pauker S G. 'Speech and Survival: Trade-offs Between Quality and Quantity of Life in Laryngeal Cancer', *New England Journal of Medicine* vol 305, no 17, 1981, pp 982–987.

ACKNOWLEDGEMENTS

This paper relates to a study, of which the author is Co-ordinator, of the costs and benefits of the cardiac transplantation programmes at Papworth and Harefield Hospitals. The study is funded by the Department of Health and Social Security and is being carried out by members of the Health Economics Research Unit, Brunel University, and the Department of Community Medicine, University of Cambridge. Parts I to V of the paper draw heavily on an unpublished preliminary report on the study provided to the DHSS. The preliminary data in Part VI are presented purely for illustrative purposes and in no way constitute a formal report of outcomes. The author wishes to thank his colleagues; Mr Terence English and Mr Madgi Yacoub; and the staff of the hospitals concerned, for their collaborative work that has made the research possible. Whilst recognising their considerable indirect contributions, this paper, and particularly Part VII, represents a personal view not necessarily shared by others involved in the research.

A history of the development of health indicators

Rachel Rosser
Charing Cross Hospital

I invite the reader to reflect on earlier chapters in this volume and to imagine a health service in which a health indicator is in routine use for evaluation and management. In the health service I have in mind, medicine has been practised in a highly specialised form for over a thousand years, and its clinicians can draw on an elaborate pharmacopoeia. Public debate has occurred about clinical responsibilities and the accountability of doctors for the results of their actions. As a consequence, a health indicator has been designed which consists of two components, a *description* of the outcomes of a number of possible health interventions, and a *scale* which expresses the relative value or importance of each so that outcomes can be expressed numerically. (These are the two basic ingredients of any health indicator.) In the health service we are considering, the indicator has been so widely accepted that it is now a statutory requirement.

What are the likely time and setting for such a system? Not, as one might imagine, Europe or North America sometime in the 21st century, but Babylon in 1792 BC, when the first heroic age of health indicators occurred.

The first heroic age
The source document is the Laws of Hammurabi, which were inscribed in Babylon, carried off to Susa, and eventually placed in the Louvre.[1,2] Figure 1 shows Hammurabi receiving the health indicator and other laws from the Sun God, Shamash.

The health indicator is defined in the following extract:

> If a surgeon has made a deep incision in the body of a man with a lancet of bronze and saves the man's life, or has opened an abscess in the eye of a man and has saved his eye, he shall take 10 shekels of silver.
> If the surgeon has made a deep incision in the body of a man with a lancet of bronze and so destroys the man's eye, they shall cut off his forehand.

There are several important principles in this law. Three outcomes are defined: death, loss of an eye and loss of a hand. These appear to be regarded as equivalent in severity and are assigned the same monetary value of 10 shekels. It is assumed that the treatment has a specific effect, and that the surgeon's skill or lack of it accounts for the outcome. The law is based upon the principle of individual clinical responsibility. The doctor is responsible for the care of the individual patient, and it appears that his survival to treat others, if he makes a mistake, is a secondary consideration. Later sections spell out that the value of an intervention depends, not only on its outcome, but also on who experiences the outcome, ie, on the characteristics of the person who receives the intervention. In

FIGURE 1   **Code of Hammurabi; Basalt Stele from Susa (The Louvre)**

Hammurabi's time the socio-economic class of the patient was particularly important; the recovery of a slave is not valued as highly as the recovery of a freeman, for example. It is also made clear that the outcomes of interventions by a variety of specialists for different conditions can all be placed on the same scale of values, and that death is not necessarily the least desirable outcome.

Figure 2 shows the utility scale incorporated in the health indicator. Although some of the underlying principles have been modified, the modern health indicator adds little to Hammurabi's model. Writing in 1972, we defined the outcome of treatment of an individual algebraically as fm_{ijt} where f is the utility assigned to the morbidity state m observed in patient i as perceived by observer j at time t.[3] This differs from Hammurabi's law in two ways. Firstly, it makes provision for different utilities to be assigned to different judges; it is thus appropriate to a democratic state. Secondly, it anticipates changes in valuations of outcome over time. In the past 4,000 years, inflation may have affected utilities and with modern help for the blind, we may not all consider that loss of an eye for example, is equivalent to death.

FIGURE 2   **Utility Scale adjusted for socio-economic group**

10	Death of freeman/Loss of eye of freeman/Loss of hand of surgeon
5	Death of nobleman/Loss of eye of nobleman/Fracture of limb of freeman/Intestinal obstruction of freeman
3	Fracture of limb of nobleman/intestinal obstruction of nobleman
2	Death of slave/Loss of eye of slave
0.2	Death of Ox
0	

The first heroic age of health indicators ended in 1750 BC. History is silent after this for 3,500 years. The Greeks and the Romans contributed little. There was a historical discontinuity, followed by a second heroic age, when the principle of health indicators was discovered again, but in a less complete form, by the Victorians, led by Florence Nightingale.

The second heroic age
On her return from Scutari, Florence Nightingale became concerned with the quality of care in hospitals which then, as now, consumed a large proportion of the resources allocated to health. In her *Notes on Hospitals*[4] she set out a system for collecting hospital statistics. This was the first use of a health indicator in hospitals. She recommended that the outcome of care be classified as 'dead', 'relieved' or 'unrelieved'. This primitive classification is a little more sophisticated than those in routine use in our hospitals today!
In recommending this method she wrote:

> I am fain to sum up with an urgent appeal for adopting this or some *uniform* system of publishing the statistical records of hospitals. There is a growing conviction that in all hospitals, even in those which are best conducted, there is a great and unnecessary waste of life. In attempting to arrive at the truth, I have applied everywhere for information, but in scarcely an instance have I been able to obtain hospital records fit for any purpose of comparison. If they could be obtained, they would enable us to decide many other questions beside the ones alluded to. They would show subscribers how their money was being spent, what amount of good was really being done with it, or whether the money was not doing mischief rather than good.

Florence Nightingale was perhaps the first person to achieve *changes*, for example in hospital design, as a consequence of applying her health indicator. Her system was implemented in a number of teaching hospitals and some continued to use it until Hospital Activity Analysis was introduced. An example is shown in Figure 3.
This shows data for two years, 1959 and 1967, for a London Hospital. In the intervening period, a new surgical block was constructed at great expense. The data show that the proportion of surgical patients classified as 'relieved' at discharge, increased from 83 per cent to 84.7 per cent. However, the corresponding figure for medical patients, who remained in the old open wards of 'Nightingale' design, rose from 70 per cent to 76 per cent. Furthermore, the proportion of both surgical and medical patients who

FIGURE 3   **Hospital data: Nightingale format**

	1959	1967
Surgical		
Relieved	83.0	84.7
Unrelieved	12.7	9.7
Dead	4.3	5.6
Medical		
Relieved	70.4	76.2
Unrelieved	22.2	14.6
Dead	7.4	9.2
Deaths		
W.L. cases	1.3	2.3
Emergencies	7.0	9.8
Emergency Ops.	1.0	6.0

died also increased. It would be impossible to attribute these changes to a particular cause. However, if we could place values on the relative importance of relief and death, we should be in a better position to comment on whether the outcomes in 1967 represented an average improvement or deterioration in comparison with 1959. In addressing this question, the Babylonian system was superior.

The modern era

The modern era, with its concern with subtle variations on the central theme, appears to aspire to classicism. It can be traced back to work, particularly by epidemiologists, in the 1930s, but the key developments have occurred in the past 20 years. Three phases can be identified: the phase of global health indicators, the phase of general health profiles and the phase of specific health profiles.

Global health indicators were developed in the late 60s and early 70s in response to the rise in demand for health care, as it became more effective and freely available, and the rise in the cost of high technology medicine, which exposed a need for measures of use in comparing the benefits of health services and allocating resources between them. Further stimulus was provided by the exchange of ideas between experts in such disparate fields as clinical medicine, epidemiology, physiology and economics, and by developments in the new field of operational research. I have recently reviewed these developments comprehensively,[5] and in this paper, I shall comment selectively. I shall not engage in a semantic discussion on the relative merits of labels such as 'measures of illness' which suggest a limited purpose, and terms such as 'indicators of quality of life' which imply a much wider application. Some researchers regard labels relating to illness or even to health, as unduly restrictive; others see the term 'quality of life' as extravagantly over-inclusive and non-specific. In practice, instruments are re-named somewhat arbitrarily, and the specifity of the instrument is not reflected in its title.

1 Global health indicators

Sullivan[6,7] writing from the Department of Health in Washington (then DHEW) brought new rigour to his review of a burgeoning literature on the measurement of quality of medical care. He discarded both clinical and subjective criteria of ill health, however important these might be for other purposes, and favoured observable and quantifiable behavioural criteria. He suggested an index constructed from a set of states of impairment of performance in social roles, expressed on a scale indicating their relative importance. He envisaged three indices; conventional expectation of life, expectation of disability-free life, and expectation of life free of bed disability. Using published survey data, he estimated these for the USA in the mid 1960s as 70 years, 65 years and 68 years respectively.

Packer[8] in a brief and seldom quoted paper defined the need for cardinal measurement. He proposed an index consisting of seven states of disability placed on a scale which measured their values relative to one another. Packer, an operational research analyst, drew on the concept of utility, which had been developed by economists and taken up by psychophysicists.

These concepts were further developed in the early 70s (reviews Berg 1973,[9] Rosser 1976,[10] Torrance 1976[11]). Four multi-disciplinary groups entered the field at the end of the 60s and published throughout the next decade. Independently and simultaneously, they all developed measures which incorporated descriptions of states of illness and cardinal scales of value. They differed in detail and in their balance between theoretical sophistication and empiricism.

Fanshel and Bush, in the USA, proposed that health should be represented by a Markov Chain model (Figure 4).[13] They conceived of an ideal life, consisting of 90 or 100 years of perfect health followed by sudden death, and graphically illustrated how a real life might depart from this ideal (Figure 5). They suggested that the impact of a treatment programme could be measured by the area between the mean functional history of a population with and without treatment (Figure 6).

An individual's state of health would be represented by the value assigned to his present state and the probability of a transition between this and all other states. Death was assigned the value of zero and was an absorbing state. The problems, apart from the minor issue of the automatic assignment of the lowest score to death, were the assumption that the value assigned to present state is independent of previous and future states, and the difficulty in assessing transitional probabilities. In later papers, Bush's group elaborated the model, defined a classification of states of illness in terms of mobility, institutionalisation, social disability, and symptom complex; explored various psychometric techniques for scaling these, usually on interval scales; and attempted by two different methods to measure the probability of transitions occurring between a limited number of states.

Torrance et al[14] developed two models for measuring the output of health care programmes. The product to be maximised was the total health of the target population, measured by the utilities assigned to a set of scenarios which described the states of people being treated in the programme. Their examples were programmes for treating tuberculosis and end stage renal failure (Figure 7).

FIGURE 4 **The prognosis or transition probability P_{IJ}.**

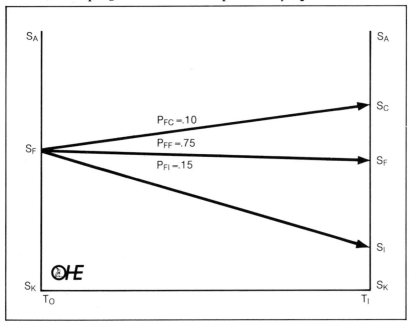

Torrance's group in Hamilton, Ontario, differed from Bush's in proceeding directly to measuring utilities, without focusing on the stage of classified descriptions. This highlighted the importance of the *concept of value* and the subsidiary role of description. In conventional measures of outcome, description is the more important stage and valuation is seldom even attempted explicitly, whereas in global indicators, description is but a stage in the process of measuring values on a cardinal scale.

FIGURE 5 **Functional history – example and ideal**

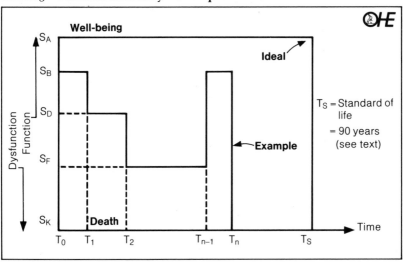

FIGURE 6   **Functional history of the population mean with and without a program. Output/person = area between curves C_w and C_o**

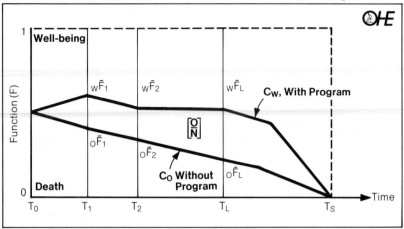

In York, a similar formulation was developed by Culyer *et al.*[15] They suggested that illness should be construed along several dimensions and conceived of curves of indifference between combinations of states along the dimensions. For example, one might be prepared to forgo some degree of activity in order to obtain some relief of painfulness (Figure 8). They also questioned whether a social consensus would emerge about the values which should be assigned.

This model was very similar to that developed by our group in London.[3,16] We devised a reliable classification of 29 states of disability and distress. These were placed on scales of utility elicited by a variety of psychometric techniques which did not imply an assumption that death is the worst possible outcome. One of the resulting scales, which appears to be ratio[17] is shown in Figure 9. This was obtained by a method of magnitude estimation, involving a 4 hour interview with each of 70 subjects[18] and has been standardised by assigning a value of 1 to freedom from disability and distress and 0 to death.[19] State 8 is defined as complete unconsciousness and it is assumed that people in this state are not actively suffering and they are therefore classified as being free of distress.

FIGURE 7   **Utility of treatments for renal failure and tuberculosis**

State	Utility
Healthy	1.00
Kidney transplant	0.83
Home dialysis	0.66
Confinement to home with TB	0.56
Hospital dialysis	0.53
Confinement to sanatorium with TB	0.34
Dead	0.00

FIGURE 8   Pain and restricted activity; indifference curves

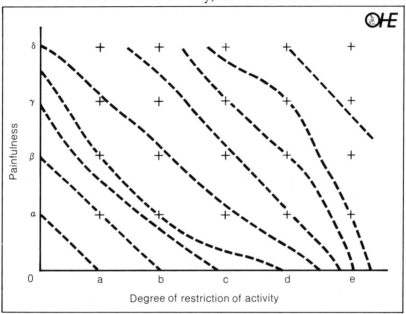

The scale reveals a diagonal relationship between states of disability and distress.

Our psychometric judges had different experiences of illness and we found that this was the only characteristic of the judge which was associated with differences in scales of value. Age, religion and social class seemed irrelevant. Psychiatric patients and the psychiatric nurses placed much emphasis on the more severe states; medical nurses and medical patients less so. Healthy volunteers, who might be planners, represented an intermediate view. Patients, nurses and doctors all considered more states to be worse than death than healthy volunteers.

FIGURE 9   Psychometric scale of values of states of disability and distress

| Disability | Distress | | | |
	1	2	3	4
1	1.000	0.995	0.990	0.967
2	0.990	0.986	0.973	0.932
3	0.980	0.972	0.956	0.912
4	0.964	0.956	0.942	0.870
5	0.946	0.935	0.900	0.700
6	0.875	0.845	0.680	0.000
7	0.677	0.564	0.000	−1.486
8	−1.028			

E

This scale was used in two hospital studies, in which more than 3,000 patients were classified, and it proved to be sensitive to differences between medical teams and to changes in patients' states over time. We found the measure to be robust. For example, the differences in scales from different sources are fascinating, but when the scales are applied to patients, they do not lead to different conclusions about services. By contrast, artificial scales based on arbitrary assumptions do lead to different results. Thus the laborious process of psychometric measurement appears to be unavoidable.

2   General health profiles

Health profiles developed in reaction to the earlier emphasis, in health indicator design, on valuation at the expense of description. In their early stages, they offered more detailed measures, appropriate to epidemiological and clinical evaluation, and thus represented a compromise between traditional measures of outcome and global health indicators. Accounts of this approach are contained in the chapters by Buxton and McEwen, and a critique is offered by Hurst, whose views on the limitations of profiles accord with mine.

In the profile approach as originally developed, many states, which may number 100 or more, are graded on a set of interval scales of severity and an individual's state of health is represented by his score on each dimension of the profile. The Symptom Impact Profile (SIP) designed by Bergner's group is the best known of these.[20] It was one of the early sources of work at Nottingham on Health Profiles (Martini et al).[21] The original SIP has been modified for use in England, re-scaled, renamed as the Function Limitation Profile (FLP) and applied to data on patients in Lambeth by a team led by Patrick (Charlton et al).[22] The clear need for more detailed descriptions, even at the expense of higher levels of measurement, is illustrated by the fact that the SIP was the measure chosen for incorporation into the important American trial of the use of oxygen in treating obstructive airways disease (Nocturnal Oxygen Trial).[23] A similar instrument was designed and applied by Sackett et al[24] but it has not been used so extensively by other groups. Both Sackett and Patrick had previously worked on global indicators, and it seems regrettable that they have pursued profiles as an alternative, rather than a complementary strategy.

In the UK, the distinction between profiles and indicators has never been as clear, as the same groups have worked on both. Advances in psychometric scaling techniques, which enable us to place more elaborate descriptions on aggregate cardinal scales have further blurred the boundaries between the two approaches.

Taking the profile approach, the Nottingham group[25] defined six dimensions of health, each with 10 subsidiary levels. McEwen has so far declined to aggregate scores along these separate dimensions to yield a global indicator, and he has refrained from commenting on some criticisms of his scaling techniques.[26] However, the profile is much simpler than the SIP and offers a compromise between comprehensiveness and sensitivity on the one hand, and brevity and economy on the other, which is attractive to clinical researchers.

Williams,[27] although aiming for the theoretical ideal of an aggregate cardinal scale of utility, placed great emphasis on the need for a reliable classification of the states of patients. He did not aim for comprehensive-ness, but worked towards a set of standard descriptions of the states of the elderly. He was also concerned with the practical problems of implement-ing these measures which proved to be considerable. Wright, working with Williams[28,29] developed a detailed classification of states of the elderly, placed these states on an ordinal scale, applied them to patients and showed that conclusions about changes in the states of patients were sensi-tive to the scale which was chosen. This instrument is more detailed and specialised than the typical health profile.

Kind and Rosser[30] elicited 70 descriptors, other than disability and dis-tress, which were judged to be important in assigning utilities to the states of patients. Forty of these were placed on an interval scale by 150 subjects with different personal experiences of illness. This exercise yielded a 40 dimensional profile subsumed by a modification of our original two dimen-sional indicator. The 40 items have also been scaled multi-dimensionally (Kind, PhD Thesis, in preparation).

Several points of interest arise from this study:
  i) There is a high level agreement about the most important descriptors, which are disability, machine dependence, and distress, which includes breathlessness. People with medical backgrounds also assigned high priority to prognosis and to diagnosis. It is therefore possible to design a simple global indicator which finds general acceptance.
 ii) There is also agreement about descriptors which are *not* important. For example, the religion and social class of the patient do not have a signi-ficant effect on the utility assigned to his state. (In holding this view, our subjects differ from Babylonians of the 2nd millenium BC!)
iii) There is little agreement about intermediate descriptors which would normally appear in a profile. There is therefore an inevitable element of expediency in the selection of items for a profile.
 iv) Only 11 of the descriptors which we elicited appear in the SIP (although all 14 of the SIP dimensions are included). We conclude that the concept of a comprehensive profile will probably prove elusive.

3 Specific health profiles

The evidence quote above suggests that general health profiles will tend to comprise somewhat arbitrary selections of items, chosen because they des-cribed the outcomes which interest the investigator. This finding is impor-tant for clinical and pharmacological research. It opens up the possibility of choosing specific, clinically relevant, outcome criteria, placing them on scales of value, and aggregating profiles of results from clinical trials so that general conclusions can be drawn about the relative efficacy of treatments which yield different patterns of benefit. In other words, the principles of the global health indicator and the general profile can be applied to highly specific data sets obtained from clinical trials.

I have recently developed these ideas in the context of psychotherapy research, a field in which multiple outcome measures have increasingly been recognised as essential.[31] Figure 10 presents an example from a recent pyschotherapy trial illustrating problems in interpreting the results of changes in several measures.

Four different types of therapy, given to breathless patients with chronic

FIGURE 10 **Outcome of psychotherapy in chronic bronchitis**

Change/Group	Control	Nurse	Supportive	Analytic
Breathlessness	—	Sustained improvement	—	—
Smoking	—	Polarised	—	Decreased
Psychiatric morbidity	Transient improvement	—	Sustained improvement	—
Depression	—	Sustained deterioration	—	—
Focal Conflict Resolution (Score 0)	—	31%	50%	44%

bronchitis, yielded four profiles consisting of different benefits and disadvantages. It is not clear which is the best treatment. To choose between them, it is necessary to rate the outcomes on cardinal scales and to measure the relative importance, or utility, of each dimension of outcome. We are encountering similar difficulties in interpreting new data from a trial of anxiolytics in the treatment of breathlessness.

Conclusions

Health indicators have reached a most interesting stage. They were designed in response to the need for better instruments for the management of health services and for higher level political judgements about resource allocation, but now seem likely to be developed more for use in clinical research. I think the reasons for this are two-fold:

i) Problems of management in the health services.

Accurate information about the *input* of resources, such as use of bed days, is not yet available to those who dispose of them, and thus more sophisticated measures of *output* can hardly be justified.

ii) Development in clinical research yielding research profiles.

Clinical and pharmacological researchers will increasingly incorporate three new types of measure into their trials. 1) A global health indicator which will be quick and economical to use, somewhat insensitive to the marginal changes reached in the typical trials, but useful in lending perspective to the results of one trial compared with other trials and with alternative developments in services. 2) A more detailed general health profile to provide a more sensitive instrument for between-trial comparisons. Preferably, the chosen indicator will subsume the elements of the profile. 3) Profiles designed for a specific trial measured on cardinal scales of utility which can be aggregated. These will be sensitive to the changes detectable in the particular trial and will ensure that an overall conclusion is drawn from a trial which yields apparently complex and conflicting data.

In the longer term, if utility measurement becomes a commonplace way of aggregating data from research profiles, clinical researchers, who also have a role as clinical managers, will demand better management information. They will want to know the utility of the outcomes predicted as consequences of alternative decisions about the allocation of health service resources. In this way, health indicators may come full circle and be brought back, by clinical researchers, to take their place as instruments for health service evaluation and management.

REFERENCES

1 Pritchard J B (ed)(1955). *Ancient Near Eastern Texts.* Princeton University Press.

2 Thorwald J (1962). *Science and Secrets of Early Medicine.* Thames and Hudson.

3 Rosser R M and Watts V C (1972). The Measurement of Hospital Output. *International Journal of Epidemiology*, 1, 361–67.

4 Nightingale F (1863). *Notes on Hospitals.* (3rd ed) Longman, Roberts and Green, London.

5 Rosser R M (1983). Issues of Measurement in the Design of Health Indicators: A Review. Chapter in *Health Indicators*, 34–81, (ed) C J Culyer. Martin Robertson, London.

6 Sullivan, D F (1966). *Conceptual Problems in Developing an Index of Health.* US Department of Health, Education and Welfare. Publication No (HRA) 74–1017, Series 2, No 5.

7 Sullivan D F (1971). *A Single Index of Mortality and Morbidity.* HMSHA Health Reports, 347–55.

8 Packer A H (1968). Applying Cost-Effectiveness Concepts to the Community Health System. *Operations Research*, 16, 227–53.

9 Berg R L (1973). *Health Status Indexes.* Hospital Research and Education Trust, Chicago.

10 Rosser R M (1976). Recent Studies using a Global Approach to Measuring Illness. *Medical Care Supplement 14*, No 5, 138–47.

11 Torrance G W (1976). Health Status Index Models: A Unified Mathematical View. *Management Science*, 22, 990–1001.

12 Fanschel S (1972). A Meaningful Measure of Health for Epidemiology. *Int J Epidemiol*, 1, 319–37.

13 Fanshel S and Bush J W (1970). A Health Status Index and its Application to Health Service Outcomes. *Operations Research*, 18, 1021–66.

14 Torrance G W, Thomas W H and Sackett D L (1971). A Utility Maximisation Model for Evaluation of Health Care Programs. *Health Services Research*, 7, 118–33.

15 Culyer A J, Lavers R J and Williams A (1971). Social Indicators: Health. *Social Trends*, 31–42. Her Majesty's Stationery Office.

16 Rosser R M and Watts V C (1976). The Measurement of Illness. *Journal of the Operational Research Society*, 29, 6, 529–40.

17 Kind P and Rosser R M (1983). Valuation of the Severity of Illness: Ratio and Interval Scales from the Same Data Set. Submitted for publication.

18 Rosser R M and Kind P K (1978). A Scale of Valuations of States of Illness: Is there a Social Consensus? *Int J Epidemiol* 7, 347–57.

19 Kind P, Rosser R M and Williams A (1982). Valuation of Quality of Life: Some psychometric evidence. In: *The Value Life and Safety*, pp 159–70, M W Jones-Lee (ed), N. Holland Pub Co.

20 Bergner M, Bobbit R A, Kressel S, Pollard W E, Gilson B S and Morris J (1976). The Sickness Impact Profile: Conceptual Formulation and Methodological Development of a Health Status Index. *International Journal of Health Services*, 6, 393–415.

21 Martini C J, Allan G J B, Davison J and Backett E M (1977). Health Indexes Sensitive to Medical Care Variation. *International Journal of Health Services*, 7, (2), 293–309.

22 Charlton J R H, Patrick D L and Peach H (1983). Use of multivariate measures of disability in health surveys. Submitted for publication.

23 Nocturnal Oxygen Therapy Trial Group (1980). Continuous or Nocturnal Oxygen Therapy in Hypoxemic Chronic Obstructive Lung Disease. *Ann Int Med* 93, 391–98.

24 Sackett D L, Chambers L W, MacPherson A S, Goldsmith C H and Macauley R G (1977). The Development and Application of Indices of Health: General Methods and a Summary of Results. *American Journal of Public Health*, 67, 423–27.

25 McKenna S P, Hunt S M and McEwan J (1981). Weighting the seriousness of perceived health problems using Thurstone's methods of paired comparisons. *International Journal of Epidemiology. 10*, 93–97.

26 Kind P (1982). A Comparison of Two Models for Scaling Health Indicators. *International Journal of Epidemiology*, 11, 3, 271–75.

27 Williams A (1974). Measuring the Effectiveness of Health Care Systems. *British Journal of Preventive and Social Medicine*, 28, 196–202.

28 Wright K G (1974). Alternative Measures of Output of Social Programmes: The Elderly, in Culyer A J (ed), *Economic Policies and Social Goals*, pp 239–72.

29 Wright K G (1978). Output measurement in practice in economic aspects of health services. (ed) Culyer A J and Wright K G, pp 46–64, Martin Roberston, London

30 Kind P and Rosser R M (1983). Global and Specific Indicators and Profiles of Health: Mutually Exclusive or Complementary? Submitted for publication

31 Rosser R (1983). Values in Dynamic Psychotherapy: Measurement and Social Choice. *Psychiatric Developments, 1*, 51–74.

The economic role of 'health indicators'

Alan Williams
University of York

Economists are primarily interested in efficiency, broadly interpreted to mean: ensuring that the value of what is gained from any activity outweighs the value of what has to be sacrificed. This requires us to distinguish clearly the resources which are sacrificed in conducting an activity (the inputs), the level of activity itself (throughput), and the gains from that activity (the output). We would like to be able to measure both inputs and outputs in commensurable (money) terms, for a variety of activity (ie throughput) levels, and to compare each activity with each alternative activity, and when all that is possible we are in a position to carry out fully-fledged cost-benefit analysis.

Unfortunately this is *not* always possible, and the element which most frequently resists valuation in money terms is the change in the health status of the individuals who are affected by the activity under investigation. To the extent that improvement or deterioration in health gives rise to changes in an individual's earning power or productivity, it is usually possible to find adequate measures of the value of such gains or losses, though in the context of high unemployment rates it is probable that the long term changes in earning power of the immediately relevant 'target' population are simply offset by corresponding changes in that of the rest of the population (eg if A is too ill to work any more, B, who would otherwise have been unemployed, gets his job instead, so the net effect for the community is small, even though the distributional effects upon the different individuals may be large). Difficulties arise where the work is not 'gainful employment', for instance, for most housework and for children's 'work' (eg schooling). In general economists do not regard the 'productivity' or 'human capital' approach to the valuation of health to be an adequate one, though the phenomena to which it directs attention are undoubtedly relevant, and may, in some circumstances, be very significant.

We then need to consider alternative ways forward, and that is where our interest in 'health indicators' sprang from. I think it can best be viewed from within a conceptualisation of health (largely due to Grossman) in which health is seen as an asset (or capital stock) which gives rise to a flow of services (time) which enter into all of our activities. If this stock gets too low, we die (ie the flow of 'time' ceases, for us as ordinary mortals at least!). If, on the contrary, we have a very good health stock, we enjoy an ample flow of healthy time, which shows up as having plenty of energy, as being in good spirits, and as feeling 'full of life'. In between these extremes lie those of us in less than perfect health, ranging from the mild 'off-day' to persistently painful and severe disability which effectively precludes most normal activity. In this view of the world, to be in good health is to have plenty of healthy life-expectancy, and the ideal measure of health would be one which reflected the *quality* of one's life expectancy (in a health sense) and not just its *quantity*. Let us call the unit in which such a concept of health might be counted a 'quality-adjusted-life-year' (or QALY for short).

If we had such a measure we could treat it as a unit of health benefit, rather like additional life expectancy, and add such units together, and compare gains and losses from different activities, just as one does with life-expectancy. It is, however, a more subtle measure than life-expectancy, because it could indicate that an activity which prolongs life expectancy only by severely reducing *quality* of life would score lower on a QALY index than an activity which left life expectancy unchanged but greatly increased quality of life. This seems a great improvement on many existing measures, but, of course, there are difficulties. It is to these that the rest of this chapter is directed.

The first, and fundamental, issue is to decide what we mean by 'quality of life' in this context. I shall deal with this summarily here, and assert that it has the following dimensions:
a) Physical mobility
b) Freedom from pain and distress
c) Capacity for self-care
d) Ability to engage in normal social interactions.
Physical mobility is likely to range from normal to bedridden, and is the most straightforward 'indicator' to construct. Pain-and-distress is a much more difficult dimension, and has the peculiarity that we have to separate out 'unconscious' or 'comatose' from 'normal' freedom from pain, but otherwise it too represents a continuum from negligible to severe. 'Capacity for self-care' refers to people's ability to wash, dress, feed themselves etc. which is usually 'hierarchical' thus making measurement easier. The 'ability to engage in normal social interaction' may be particularly important in some mental illness where anti-social behaviour is manifest or where people have irrational or exaggerated fears concerning contact with others. Note that these dimensions of health-as-quality-of-life make no explicit reference to the presence or absence of any morbid condition or clinical entity or recognisable syndrome, but only to feelings and functional capacities which are quite understandable to ordinary people and require no technical expertise to recognise. What will need technical expertise to recognise is *why* someone manifests those particular feelings and functional capacities, and what, if anything, might be done about it. The success of any such intervention would then be judged by its effect on those phenomena (and upon life expectancy) compared with some specified alternative 'intervention' (which might be 'no intervention').

Economists look to health indicators to provide data on each of these dimensions (and any others that may prove significant) so that the second major problem can be tackled, namely, how they can be compressed into a single index. Before discussing that, however, let us consider whether that step is strictly necessary, or whether we could not just as well work with a multi-attribute notion of health and save ourselves a lot of trouble. We could obviously save ourselves a lot of trouble if we simply 'scored' each individual 'good' *or* 'indifferent' *or* 'bad' on each of the dimensions a) to d) in the preceding paragraph, and then added a fifth dimension e) life expectancy which we treated in the same way. Even that crude characterisation would be sufficient for our purposes in a situation in which one of the activities under investigation 'dominated' all the others (ie it was better than them in at least one respect and no worse than any of them in any other respect). But such cases are likely to be rare, and where different indicators move in different directions, such simple comparisons will be inconclusive and the problem of 'trade-offs', or relative valuations, will arise. This problem could be side-stepped by the 'investigator', and left for resolution by the 'policy-maker', in which case it is the latter's (probably implicit and possibly even unconscious) valuations that will count. But what if *either* the policy maker wants guidance as to what sort of valuations the affected people hold *or* it is felt that everyone ought to know what these valuations are if for no other reason than that if they are set aside by 'the policy maker' some good reasons should be given? In such cases the investigator must go further and seek to make these valuations explicit. Note also that in this context a 'policy-maker' may be a professional person, such as a clinician, deciding what is in the best interests of some other person or persons, and need not be a 'politician' in the ordinary senses of the word.

So let us assume that we are seeking a 'global' index of health which reflects the valuations of affected or potentially affected individuals, then why not revert to the classic economist's solution of seeking valuations based on willingness and ability to pay? To a large extent this is what has happened in the 'valuation of life' literature, in which a money value of life has been elicited either from discovering people's behaviour when they can save money by increasing (or spend money on decreasing) the risks of premature death, *or* from experiments in which people are offered complicated gambles which have similar significance. If the existing distribution of income and wealth were considered a proper ethical basis for health valuations in the particular 'political' context in which the data is to be used, then this 'solution' to the valuation of a QALY would be very useful, since it generates a money value directly, and gets us right back to where we want to be. Unfortunately, such work has, so far, been concerned almost exclusively with quantity of life, not with quality. A more fundamental problem, however, is that its valuations will in any case be unacceptable in those situations where it is held as a matter of principle that the valuation of health should not depend on ability to pay.

So now we come to that part of the health indicators work which has attempted to construct an index of health by comparing the relative valuations attached to different health states, where one health state is declared to be the basis of comparison (say treated as the unit 1) and all others rated relatively to it. In economists' parlance this is tantamount to creating a utility index across states of health, where a 'state of health' is a combination of the characteristics outlined earlier under the headings a) to d). Such an index may be merely ordinal (better/worse) but for our purposes we really need something more ambitious, so that we can perform normal mathematical manipulations such as addition and division upon it. The history of the development of such measures has been dealt with by Rachel Rosser, so I will not go further into all that here.

Instead let me turn to an important ethical issue about aggregation. In most clinical trials it is commonplace to add together years-of-life-gained, irrespective of who gains them, and this implies a strong ethical position that one year of additional life is of equal value to everybody, no matter who they are, or what their age or sex. Strong though that position is, it is probably as acceptable as any alternative ethical position as a basis for public policy. If we see the development of health indicators as the development of the 'QALY', and the 'QALY' as a more discriminating version of the additional-year-of-life, then we might assert that a *healthy* year of additional life expectancy should, by analogy, be treated as of equal value to everybody, irrespective of age, sex or social condition, and let each person develop their own relative values for non- healthy states from that common base. Thus the 'quality-adjustments' are personal and based on the views of individuals, but the aggregation process is common, and socially determined.

Finally let me consider how such an index would be used within the context of an economic appraisal designed to choose the more cost-effective of a range of options. In such a context the differential benefits in health terms from the different options would be represented by a 'points' score derived from the index described earlier (where 1 'point' = 1 year of healthy life expectancy for someone). The differential 'costs' associated with each option would be separately measured, and would include, as *negative* costs, any differential resource *gains* associated with the options (for instance, if one option reduced time off work much more than any others, the corresponding output gains would show up as reductions in the costs of that option). For each option we would then have a 'health' score and a net cost figure, and the preferred option would be that which had the highest ratio of points to costs (ie the one which is most 'cost-effective', where 'effectiveness' is measured by the health index).

One final caveat is in order. At the outset I stressed that ideally we need to know the *value* of benefits in terms commensurable with the *value* of the resources sacrificed (ie the costs). To get to that situation here we would still need to place a value on an index point. Once this step has been taken we are in a position to conduct full-scale cost-benefit analysis. It could be taken by the policy-maker postulating such a value (ie deciding that a year of healthy life expectancy is worth, say, £10,000) which would mean that in his judgement it is worth committing £10,000 of the community's resources to achieve that benefit. This is effectively what happens within the road investment programme (but not in the health service). Until this step is taken we would *not* be able to infer from an economic appraisal of the cost-effectiveness type that *any* of the options under consideration is really worth undertaking, for all that a cost-effectiveness study can tell us is which of the options under consideration is best . . . and, in this limited context, the best may not be good enough!

In summary, then, what economists seek from the work on health indicators is a global index of health which can be used in cost-effectiveness studies as a measure of effectiveness. The more comprehensive it can be in terms of the dimensions of health it incorporates; the more sensitive it can be in terms of its responsiveness to an individual's perceptions of the value of health; and the more practical it can be in terms of the feasibility of collecting and analysing the relevant information within the orbit of a clinical trial; the more attractive it is as a complement to the resource valuation which has hitherto been the conventional role of the economist in such work. We are anxious to ensure that benefits and costs get more symmetrical and integrated treatment in such studies, and it is essentially from that concern that our interest in health indicators stems.

Measurement of the benefits in psychiatry

David Goldberg
University of Manchester

Until comparatively recently, psychiatrists had assumed that the aim of psychiatric treatment services was to reduce distress and disability caused by mental illness, and to do what they could to improve the social and interpersonal functioning of their patients in hopes that this would improve the mental health of their patients and reduce the probability of relapse. It may have appeared reasonable to assess the benefits of a particular treatment by measuring the social and clinical status of a group of treated patients before and after treatment using some of the many standardised assessment scales available, and to assume that improvement in the ratings obtained could be attributed to the effects of the treatment. This approach to the measurement of benefit fails to solve three problems.

First, it is worth remembering that the model of treatment aimed at producing states of complete freedom from distress is inappropriate for residential programmes for patients such as severely handicapped children, 'old long-stay' chronic psychotic patients, and elderly severely demented patients. The effect of the treatment programme in minimising disability and social dysfunction may be expressed as a *deterioration* in absolute terms, but a smaller deterioration than might have been expected had the treatment service not existed. This brings us to our second problem. Comparisons of a single group of patients before and after treatment are meaningless unless we know the natural history of the condition: in order to measure benefits we must always compare two groups of patients, the comparison group being *either* a 'no-treatment' control group or a group who have had some conventional treatment. The spontaneous remission rates for various mental illnesses are widely variable. The third problem is that if we confine our measurements to social and clinical measures it does not enable us to make rational decisions concerning resource allocation. Psychiatric treatments have economic as well as social and clinical benefits, and it is important to measure these since it may be justifiable to spend more on services to achieve greater economic benefits to the community at large.[1,2,3] The arrival of economic measures of outcome has attracted attention towards aspects of benefit that had previously been neglected: for example, the importance of returning patients back to employment early, and the implications of certain treatments in conferring benefits over many years.

Alternative measures of benefit in psychiatry
The unthinking investigator has no clear hypothesis and measures everything in sight: symptoms of illness, disabilities and defects consequent upon illness, social adjustment of the patient – all these in both the patient and his living group – as well as characteristics of the treatment services themselves. If enough things are measured the hope is that any important effect

will show up, and something will turn out to be significant. However, unless the investigator has no idea about the likely non-monetary benefits of a particular service, it is undoubtedly better to concentrate the evaluation on those aspects of outcome that are likely to be affected.

For example, if we are concerned with the benefits produced by a new antidepressant drug it will be sufficient to measure outcome with symptom scales focused on the phenomena of depressive illness, but if we are concerned with the effectiveness of an additional psychotherapeutic treatment of depression it will be necessary to include other measures of outcome that are relevant to the rationale of the new treatment. Thus we might include relapse rate and self esteem as outcome measures of the benefits produced by cognitive therapy for depression, and scales of satisfaction and social function in the assessment of interpersonal therapy (IPT) for depression. Scales measuring disabilities, defects and social adjustment are particularly relevant in the assessment of services for ambulant psychotic patients discharged in the community. In Wing's hostel ward comparison for example, where the patients in the comparison were all institutionalised, the evaluation included a patient's attitude scale and a time budget as well as a social adjustment scale, since it was anticipated that the new service might produce advantages in these areas.[4]

The importance of a clearly stated aim

Although it is usual to carry out comprehensive social and clinical assessments in two groups of comparable patients, the data produced by such assessments should be considered under two headings, the 'stated aims' of the evaluation and 'other effects'. First, did the new service achieve its intended aims? In order to measure this aspect of benefit we must assume that the service being evaluated has clearly stated aims, and that we have used rating scales which are relevant to these aims. The remainder of the data generated by the social and clinical assessments are used to ensure that any advantages of the experimental service are not at the cost of other unanticipated disadvantages, and to test for any unpredicted advantages that the new service might have. In this part of the data analysis there will be large numbers of analyses of which some will be significant by chance: in contrast any test in the former group which is significant can be interpreted more easily.

If the clinical status of a patient is expressed as a score on a symptom scale it is important that the scale is homogenous in the sense of being a measure of a single dimension. It would therefore be reasonable to express outcome as a score on, say, the Beck Depression Inventory; but it would be unreasonable to express it as 'total score' on an overall measure of psychopathology such as the 'present state evaluation' or the 'diagnostic interview schedule'. Where such comprehensive clinical assessments are used in evaluation, the only reasonable procedure would appear to be to compare the responses of the two groups taking the various ratings one at a time.

The measurement of economic benefits

In a conventional cost-benefit analysis all the effects of a service are in principle quantified and expressed in monetary terms.[5] If the benefits (monetary value of the advantages) exceed the costs (monetary value of the disadvantages), then a cost-benefit analysis implies that the service should be implemented. If two or more services are being compared, then a common decision rule is that the service with the most advantageous cost/benefit ratio should be selected. Cost-benefit analysis may be either focused on a particular problem or used to obtain rough priorities among major alternative models of service. However, it is necessary to carry out an exhaustive measurement of all costs and benefits that can be expressed in monetary terms. It is here that the major problem arises with cost-benefit analysis, since treatment programmes typically concern themselves with aims that cannot really be expressed in financial terms, such as the relief of symptoms and distress and improvement in psychosocial adjustment. The requirement that all the effects of a given service should be expressed in monetary terms deflects attention from those aspects of service which cannot be valued in this way, and makes the philistine assumption that utility and value march hand in hand.

One solution to the problem has been to attempt to measure all benefits in economic terms. Rosser and Watts produce a set of weights for various combinations of distress and disability, which are themselves derived from current compensation payments made by British Courts.[6]

Binner, Halpern and Potter have also attempted to place cash values on soft benefits of treatment at the Fort Logan Mental Health Center, Denver.[7,8] For each patient, they calculate 'an economic value of the patient's response to the programme as a function of his impairment at time of admission and his level of response at discharge. This component, called the response value, estimates the economic value of the intangible benefits of treatment skills that are so often ignored in evaluation studies.' In order to obtain the response value, the investigators compute a coefficient based on the degree of improvement, and multiply this by $10,000. The authors do not state how the latter figure was arrived at, and it is unclear whether such figures can really be used to calculate sums of money that can be reasonably added and subtracted from other, more real, sums of money.

Nor are the investigators always pleased with their own success at reducing everything to cash. Binner, Halpern, and Potter state that 'concern stems from a desire to treat the values measured as 'real dollars'. . . . This means that a programme which treats largely schizophrenics may not be able to show as favourable a rate of return on investment as one which treats primarily neurotic patients. . . . Programmes serving such different populations should not be comparatively judged on the absolute rates of return involved.'

If we were to allow ourselves to become preoccupied with economic measures of benefit resources would be switched towards highly treatable disorders such as acute depression in those with high earning ability, and away from chronic deteriorating disorders in those who are unemployed or unemployable. The attempt to express all the output of a service in economic terms makes for a result which is easy to interpret, but prevents us from considering important aspects of a service which have no economic consequences.

Let us consider a comparison between two residential homes for demented old people. We will assume that each has the same staff and overhead expenses, and neither is so poor that relations take back the old people to their own homes, thus changing the patterns of expenditure. Although the economic comparison will therefore show that the economic benefits of each are the same, it may be that one has high morale, high standards of care and high satisfaction, while the other is associated with higher levels of clinical symptomatology and disability and a low standard of care, despite the fact that patients were allocated to the two homes at random. It is clear that economic measures cannot be allowed to be the sole measures of benefit in psychiatry.

Glass and Goldberg have suggested a modification to the traditional cost-benefit framework in which investigators who wish to compare two services carry out a conventional cost-benefit analysis, but measure the soft costs and benefits a a separate exercise.[9] The results of the economic comparison can be condensed to a single figure called the 'Net Effect' of the comparison between two services, and this is then used to interpret the overall balance sheet of soft costs and benefits. If a service which produces more 'soft' benefits is also cheaper, then it is said to 'dominate' the other service; while if the service with more soft benefits is more expensive, health planners will at least have objective data to help them decide whether the extra quality is worth the extra price.[2,10] There are a number of limitations to such studies. Firstly, this sort of comparison cannot say whether it is worth having a service at all; it can only say which of the two services is preferable. By the same token, there may be some third way of running the service which is better than either of the services that have been compared. Secondly, although the economic analysis may be helpful in showing us which component parts of a particular service contribute to its economic efficiency, it cannot tell us which aspects of the service are responsible for any 'soft' advantages that it may have. Finally, this type of evaluation demands lengthy and painstaking observations on the patients, and perhaps largely for this reason it has not so far been widely followed.

Nevertheless, the design is a powerful one, and it enables the following statements to be made:

1 The more expensive service, with higher doctor:patient ratios and per diem costs, was very much cheaper from the standpoint of the community.
2 The economic benefits of the district general hospital service (DGH) were long lasting: they are well seen three to four years into the illness, but are even more striking 10 to 12 years into the illness.
3 The clinical benefits of the DGH service were striking 10 to 12 years later, in that there were fewer schizophrenic defect states in the DGH service than in the service associated with the mental hospital.

The duration of benefits
Conventional evaluations of drug treatments are directed at advantages that accrue to patients while they are on a particular treatment, and tend to ignore benefits that may outlast the particular treatment, or which would not have occurred had the treatment not been given. If a conventional antidepressant produces symptom relief in 65 per cent of patients, and a new drug achieves the same level of success in 75 per cent, we tend to forget

that the advantages enjoyed by this 10 per cent of extra patients may continue to last for substantial time periods. The arrival of economic methods of analysis has undoubtedly focused attention on such effects, since special methods of analysis ('discounting') must be used to take account of them.

It seems likely that these time periods can be substantial, and certainly considerably longer than the duration of a particular treatment trial. For example, Johnstone and Goldberg showed that merely making a family doctor aware of a high score on a screening questionnaire produced significant levels of symptom reduction in the ensuing six months, and that the spontaneous recovery rate in the untreated control group only produced comparable reductions in symptoms 12 months later: while for patients with more than 20 symptoms at initial consultation, differences were still significant a year later.[11] Marks has recently shown that a subset of patients seen in primary care settings with specified behavioural patterns will not improve significantly if left untreated for a year, and clinical experience of patients seen in this setting suggests that this is also true of many untreated depressives in the community.[3] We have already seen that the Manchester schizophrenia study showed substantial long term effects of two types of treatment: it seems likely that in schizophrenia economic effects of different treatments may be detectable over the working life of the patients.

Indicators of the quality of psychiatric services
We have so far emphasised the importance of evaluating the benefits produced by psychiatric treatment by taking two or more comparable cohorts of patients, and making relevant clinical and social assessments of outcome, together with economic observations about the costs and benefits of the services to the patient and his family on the one hand, and the rest of the community on the other. It is worth remembering that although satisfaction with the service experienced by patients and their relatives is sometimes included as a benefit, there are certain problems in interpreting the results. One problem is that a good service may make previously contented, institutionalised chronic patients more critical of the care they receive, and thus more dissatisfied with it.[4] Another problem is that the determinants of patient-satisfaction are likely to be different from those of economic effectiveness on the one hand, and clinical effectiveness on the other.

Let us consider twelve possible indicators of the quality of a psychiatric service:

Indicators of quality that can be obtained easily in a comparison between two services:
1 Waiting time to be seen in the clinic.
2 Quality of buildings and furnishings.
3 Efficiency and courtesy of receptionists and clinic nurses.
4 Adequacy of training of paramedical staff.
5 Availability and use of a wide range of treatments: medical, psychological and social.
6 Extent of undesirable practices (eg physical restraint, seclusion rooms, excessive ECT, excessive use of compulsory powers, over-sedation).
7 Extent of desirable practices (eg accessibility and friendliness of staff, frequency patient is seen by qualified staff).

8 Full range of rehabilitation facilities freely available.

There are some *additional indicators that could only be assessed by clinically experienced independent research workers:*

9 Thoroughness of assessment interview.
10 Quality of doctor's interview skills.
11 Sophistication of formulations, adequacy of notes.
12 Appropriateness of treatment offered.

It is not clear that the latter group of indicators would add very much to the information more easily obtained by the first eight, and they would undoubtedly be more difficult to obtain. We can now see that client satisfaction is likely to be determined by a different group of indicators than those which determine clinical and economic effectiveness: indeed, 'waiting time' is probably the only indicator that is related to all three. Client satisfaction is likely to be determined by indicators 1, 2, 3 and 7, and perhaps by 6. Economic effectiveness is likely to be largely determined by 1, 5 and 12, with other indicators being only related indirectly. Finally, clinical effectiveness is not likely to be much affected by indicators 2 and 3, but is otherwise determined by the widest range of indicators.

Conclusions

1 *The importance of a clear aim*
The way in which we choose to measure the benefit of a psychiatric treatment will depend on the aim of that treatment, and we must use rating scales and measures that are relevant to that aim.

2 *The importance of a comparison group*
It is argued that it is impossible to assess the benefits of a new treatment unless we compare the results of this treatment with either the results of an established treatment or with no treatment. (Only the latter will tell us whether it is worth having any treatment.)

3 *The importance of economic measures of benefit*
If our assessments of the benefits produced by treatment are to produce modifications to existing services which involve increased expenditure it is advisable to include such measures. Such analyses remind us that psychiatric treatments may exert important benefits over long periods of time, and such effects may be important in choosing between different forms of treatment.

REFERENCES
1 Wadsworth W, Tonge W and Barber L. The cost and efficiency of mental hospitals. *Lancet,* 2, 533–534 1957.
2 Goldberg D and Jones R. The Costs and Benefits of Psychiatric Care. In *Ed* Robins L. 'The Social Consequence of Psychiatric Illness'. Brunner-Mazel, NY, 1980.
3 Marks I. Report to the DHSS on the economic consequences of behavioural therapy by nurse therapists in the community (1983).
4 Wing J and Wykes J. Long-term community care: experience in a London Borough. *Psych Med Mono Suppl. No* 2 pp 59–97.
5 Williams A and Anderson R. Efficiency in the Social Services. Blackwell, 1974.
6 Rosser R and Watts V. The development of a classification of morbidity and its use to measure the output of a hospital, SSRC Conference, 1973. Quoted in A Williams and R Anderson, Efficiency in the Social Services. Oxford: Blackwell, 1975.

F

7 Binner R, Halpern J and Potter A. Patients, programs and results in a comprehensive mental health center. *J Cons Clin Psychol, 41*, 148–156 1973.

8 Potter A, Binner P and Halpern J. Readmission discount factors in program evaluation. *Am J Comm Psychol, 3,* 305–314 1975.

9 Glass N and Goldberg D. Cost-benefit analysis and the evaluation of psychiatric services. *Pyschol Med, 7,* 701–707 1977.

10 Jones R, Goldberg D and Hughes B. A comparison of two different services treating schizophrenia: a cost-benefit appraoch. *Psychol Med, 10,* 493–505 (1980).

11 Johnstone A and Goldberg D. Psychiatric screening in general practice. *Lancet* i, 605–608, 1976.

The Nottingham health profile: a measure of perceived health

Jim McEwen

King's College Hospital, London

Introduction

Information on how people feel as opposed to how they become ill and what they die from is scarce: there is an absence of direct measures of health. There have been many calls in recent years for socio-medical or sub-jective indicators of health which could be used as a standard measure of self assessed health, both for use as a population survey tool and as an aid to individual clinical care. Since it is perceived, and not necessarily actual problems which lead to demand for health care, a measure of perceived health would seem to be an essential component of planning health care. Similarly, perceived health measured in a standard form must be regarded as a valuable indicator of the effectiveness of any form of intervention – medical, surgical or social.

There have been many attempts to develop a standard measure of self-assessed health for use as a population survey tool. It was hoped that such indicators would be capable of measuring the health status of whole populations at a particular point in time; of providing reliable repeated measures over time, and of assessing the efficacy of health care. Many of the attempts have encountered problems of definition, measurement, weighting, reliability, validity, sensitivity and specificity. While some instruments have been long, complex and comprehensive, others have been narrow and have concentrated on one or more specific aspects of disability.

Any population survey tool should be understood by a large majority of potential respondents, be short and simple to answer, cheap to administer, easy to score, be valid and reliable, should not be too sophisticated, should be sensitive enough to assess health need and specific enough for the evaluation of health care provision for specific groups.[1] Bearing such criteria in mind an attempt has been made to produce a completely new measure of perceived health, rather than an adaptation of an existing instrument.

Development

In 1975, a research team, with funds from the Social Science Research Council started work on a 'quality of life' measure – a socio-medical indicator – which would describe the typical effects of ill health, physical, social and emotional. The reasons for developing the measure were:
- to provide some assessments of a person's need for care which was not based upon purely medical criteria.
- to enable the subsequent evaluation of care provided for persons in need.
- to make a start on the development of an indicator which could be used for the survey of population health status.

The team began by conducting a number of interviews, 768 in all, with patients having a variety of acute and chronic ailments. From these interviews, a total of 2,200 statements were extracted which described the typical effects of ill health. These effects encompassed social, psychological, behavioural and physical functions. The statements were grouped into categories according to the function described – sleeping, eating, movement, social life, emotional reactions and so on. The wording of each statement was scrutinised for redundancy, ambiguity, esoteric expressions and reading age. This reduced the number of statements to 138.

Combinations of these remaining statements were used in a number of pilot studies on different populations, enabling the statements to be further reduced and refined. By relating scores on the questionnaire to medical information and independent assessments of patient's well-being, as well as other standardized measures, it was found that the items were reliable and valid in distinguishing between different degrees of disability and sensitive to change over time. In addition they were able to distinguish between physical and mental disorders.[2,3,4] A final pool of 82 items covering 12 domains of functioning was obtained. The items had indicated their value in reflecting subjective states and providing a measure of perceived impairment.

In 1978, a further grant was obtained from the Social Science Research Council to develop the existing instrument into a 'population survey tool'.[5] This meant refining the criteria by which statements were chosen for inclusion in the questions, and statements were re-examined, retested and analysed using the following criteria:
– there should be no negative expressions.
– statements should be easy to understand, unambiguous and easy to answer.
– statements should be answerable by 'yes' or 'no'.
– language should conform to standards of a minimum reading age.
Items which met these standards were tested on patient and non-patient groups and those which proved satisfactory were retained.

The profile
Part I of the Profile comprises 38 items which meet the stringent criteria and which best reflected problems with health. They fall into six areas:

sleep

physical mobility

energy

pain

emotional reactions

social isolation

Within each area, statements have been weighted using the Thurstone method of paired comparisons.[6] The weights reflect the perceived severity of the items from the consensus point of view.

Part II of the Profile consists of seven statements relating to these areas of daily life most often affected by health:

paid employment

looking after the house

social life

home life

sex life

hobbies and interest

holidays

The respondent simply indicates 'yes' or 'no' according to whether the statement applies to him or her 'in general'. In Part I the weights given to the questions are adjusted so that the maximum score on any section is 100.

Such a score would indicate that the respondent had every problem listed in the section. Statements in Part II are scored for an affirmative response and zero for a negative.

Administration

The Profile was designed to be self-administered and very few problems will be encountered using it this way. It is also possible to read out the statements to individuals who have sight or reading problems. The Profile can be administered either to an individual or on a group basis. Studies in which the Profile has been sent by post have yielded response rates between 68 per cent and 93 per cent. Its success as a postal questionnaire is highly dependent upon the population being sampled, appropriate preparatory discussions and the content and source of the covering letter. The Profile can be used with populations aged 16 years and over and requires a minimum reading age of 10 years.

The scoring and analysis of the results are described in a manual which is being prepared. This contains a format suitable for analysis using the statistical package for the social sciences. Preliminary age, sex and social class norms are included in the manual although it is intended that further studies will be used to provide an enlarged sample for the calculation of norms.

Testing

The Profile has been tested for face, content and criterion validity with groups of elderly people of differing clinical condition,[7] with patients who consult their general practitioners,[8] with firemen,[9] mine rescue workers,[10] pregnant women, patients undergoing minor surgery and fracture victims.[11]

Two studies[11] were carried out to establish the relationship of Profile scores in terms of their consistency over time. Both studies utilised the test-retest technique. Since a high percentage of negative responses would give a spurious correlation, it was necessary to use groups of people who could be expected to be high scorers.

These studies indicated that the Profile was a highly satisfactory indicator of subjective health in the physical, social and emotional domains and a useful guide to the extent to which health problems are restricting customary daily activities, and it can be used, with a wide range of people and age groups.

It should be noted that the instrument has been developed, tested and used in England. Some preliminary studies are under way in other countries and using other languages, but the very nature of the instrument would suggest that to some extent it must be culture specific and that careful testing and possibly some redevelopment will be necessary before it could be used in other countries.

Clinical studies

Some of the main findings of two studies are summarised here: details will be found in published papers and reports.

1 *Subjective Health Status and Consultation Rates*
The study[8] was carried out in general practice and 352 on the practice list

were interviewed. Each interview had three parts:

a) The interviewer asked questions concering personal details, employ-ment and amount of physical activity undertaken.

b) The respondent completed the Nottingham Health Profile by him or herself.

c) Further questions were asked about absence from work, consultation of the general practitioner and overall self-rated health in the past six months and at the time of the interview.

People who had no contacts with their doctor in the past six months were defined as non-consulters, while those who had 3 or more consulta-tions or repeat prescriptions were defined as consulters.

Differences between 'consulters' and 'non-consulters' were highly signifi-cant on every section of the Profile ($p < 0.01$). Females had significantly higher mean scores than males on all sections except pain and physical mobility ($p < 0.05$). There were significant age group differences on sleep, social isolation and physical mobility due largely to higher scores obtained by the 40–49 year olds ($p < 0.05$ in all cases). Amount of physical activity at work did not relate to scores, but activity outside working hours did. Sub-jects coded in a 'little activity' category tended to score more highly on energy, pain and physical mobility sections.

Days of absence from work through ill health were significantly related to scores on every section ($p < 0.001$).

Perceived health over the previous six months and perceived health at the present time, both coded as Very Good, Good, Fair, Poor, Very Poor, were both significantly related to scores on all sections in those who saw their health as having been fair, poor or very poor, having significantly higher scores than those who perceived their health as having been very good or good.

2 *Pregnancy*

It was considered that it would be valuable to use the Profile in a setting when changes in well-being could be expected to take place over a period of time.[11] Pregnancy seemed ideal for this since it is clearly not an 'unhealthy' condition, yet it is evident from the literature that well women having a normal pregnancy experience recognisable physical, social and emotional changes over the nine month period, and that these changes follow a relatively consistent pattern. Since the aim was to look at the changes in 'normal' pregnancy, women who could be defined as 'high risk' were excluded. One hundred women were recruited for the study and data analysis is based on a sample of 80. The main scores for Part I are shown in Figure 1.

The Wilcoxon matched pairs signed ranks test showed that there was a significant increase in score on physical activity and sleep between 18 and 27 weeks; and that between 27 and 37 weeks all sections, except social isola-tion, showed a significant increase in score.

Problems were most commonly reported in physical mobility, energy and sleep; an increasing number of women experienced problems in these areas over the period of pregnancy, and the severity of the problems (as measured by score on the sections) also increased over time. Apparently

FIGURE 1   **Median scores on Part I of the profile at 18, 27 and 37 weeks of pregnancy.**

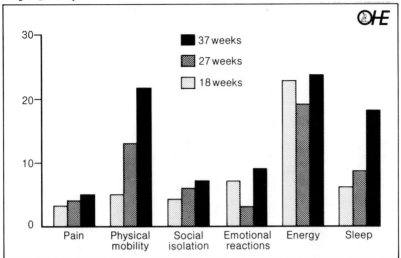

half the women at each stage reported some emotional reactions. The percentage of women reporting problems of pain rose sharply from 10 per cent at 18 weeks to 40 per cent at 37 weeks; whilst problems of social isolation remained consistently low throughout.

There was considerable variation in the proportion of women experiencing problems on the different sections. For example, only 15–20 per cent of women experienced problems of social isolation at any one time, but 89 per cent of the sample reported problems of physical mobility by 37 weeks.

On Part II of the Profile, Figure 2 illustrates the percentage of women at each gestation stage who reported that their state of health was causing problems in various areas of their daily life. The area most commonly affected was sex life and the percentage of women reporting disruption in the area increased significantly (McNemar test $p < 0.05$) between 18 and 27 weeks and between 27 and 37 weeks. Between 18 and 27 weeks an increasing number of women reported that their hobbies and interests were being affected, but it was not until 37 weeks gestation that a marked increase in problems in the areas of social life, caring for the home and holidays was recorded. Home life remained unchanged throughout, whilst reported problems in 'job of work' decreased over time, as the number of women giving up work because of the pregnancy increased.

The mean number of areas of daily life the women reported as being affected by the state of health rose from 1.1 at 18 weeks through 1.3 at 27 weeks to 1.7 at 37 weeks gestation.

The percentage of women reporting any problems on Part II increased over time, from 47 per cent at 18 weeks to 65 per cent at 37 weeks: and the amount of disruption, as measured by the number of areas affected also increased. Between 18 and 27 weeks the change was slight; the major change occurred between 27 and 37 weeks and the increase in problems over this period was statistically significant ($p < 0.05$, sign test).

FIGURE 2 **Percentage of women reporting problems in each of the seven areas of daily life at 18, 27 and 37 weeks gestation.**

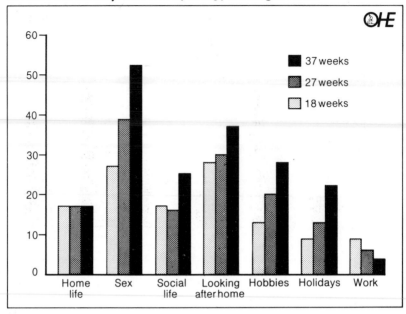

Scores on Part I and Part II reflected the pattern one would expect to see in well women during a normal pregnancy. The Profile was also able to distinguish some who experienced medical, social and psychological stresses and those who did not.

Summary
The Nottingham Health Profile is a two part, self-administered questionnaire, designed to measure perceived health and the extent to which such problems affect normal activities.

It is appropriate for use in the following ways:
– for evaluation of medical/social intervention in pre-test, post-test design.
– as an outcome measure for group comparisons.
– as a survey tool with specified groups.
– as an adjunct to the clinical interview.

A measure such as the Profile should be seen, not as a replacement for morbidity and mortality statistics or other refined indices, but as an adjunct to them. Routine data can be enriched by the input of specially collected data from target populations or even for the population as a whole. In order to aid decision-making for health care, it will be necessary to have a range of indicators which can be used to delineate more clearly needs and problems in the community. Measures of perceived and objective needs as the means of evaluating services should be built into all health information. However, it is necessary always to be reminded that the purpose of health information is to assist in the determination of the services required by the population, not to produce data for their own sake or to accumulate records for unspecified purposes.

Figures 3 and 4 set out the advantages and the limitations of the Profile. Appendix I gives the questions as actually presented to respondents. The questions in Part I are in random order, rather than being divided into their six areas. This provides some check on the validity of the answers in each of the areas covered.

In the field of health services research, it is envisaged that the Profile will be able to contribute to:
- the identification of groups in need of care.
- the development of social policy by helping to determine the allocation of resources.
- mass aspects of the evaluation of health and social services.
- the identification of consumer concerns.
- the theoretical understanding of the relationship between different subjective responses to comparable pathologies.

Applied appropriately, it is hoped that the Nottingham Health Profile will provide a much needed additional tool for clinical and epidemiology research.

FIGURE 3   **Advantages of the Profile**

1 It is suitable for use in a wide range of situations from individual clinical interviews to large scale population surveys.
2 It has high validity and reliability.
3 It is easy and cheap to administer.
4 It takes only a short time to complete and is highly acceptable to respondents.
5 It is easy to score and compute particularly if the Statistical Package for the Social Sciences is used.
6 Scores can be compared graphically.
7 It can be used to measure general perceived health status and specific conditions of ill-health.
8 Since the profile does not ask directly if people have *health* problems, it is more likely to pick up people who are ill, or at risk, but who do not perceive their problems as being related to health.
9 Since the items in the Profile refer to problems, not symptoms, there is less opportunity for respondents to 'medicalise' psychological or social stress.

FIGURE 4   **Limitations of the Profile**

1 The items on Part I represent rather severe situations. It was found necessary to do this to avoid picking up large quantities of false positives associated with less severe situations. However, this does mean that some individuals who are suffering discomfort may not show up on the Profile.
2 'Normal' populations or those with minor ailments may offer few statements on some sections. This makes it difficult to compare the scores or to be able to demonstrate change.
3 'Zero scorers' cannot be shown to improve on the Profile, although in actuality they may be feeling better than on the previous occasions.
4 The Profile does not attempt to cover all possibilities. Despite this the statements are selected to sample the universe of health problems.
5 The scores on Part II are a combination of two functions whether or not the respondent has a health problem and, if so, if it is affecting any of the specified areas. It should not be taken to mean that the individual has that area affected in the absence of a health problem.
6 Part I involves six scores plus a further seven scorres for Part II. Analysis can, therefore, become cumbersome if large numbers of other variables need to be taken into account.
7 The Profile measures health by its absence, by focusing on negative aspects of health.

Nottingham Health profile

Part I

Listed below are some problems people may have in their daily life.
Look down the list and put a tick in the box under **Yes** for any problem you have at the moment.
Tick the box under **No** for any problem you do not have.

Please answer every question. If you are not sure whether to say Yes or No, tick whichever answer you think is **more true** at the moment.

	Yes	No		Yes	No
I'm tired all the time	☐	☐	I lie awake for most of the night	☐	☐
I have pain at night	☐	☐	I feel as if I'm losing control	☐	☐
Things are getting me down	☐	☐	I'm in pain when I'm standing	☐	☐

	Yes	No		Yes	No
I have unbearable pain	☐	☐	I find it hard to dress myself	☐	☐
I take tablets to help me sleep	☐	☐	I soon run out of energy	☐	☐
I've forgotten what it's like to enjoy myself	☐	☐	I find it hard to stand for long (eg, at the kitchen sink, waiting for a bus)	☐	☐

	Yes	No		Yes	No
I'm feeling on edge	☐	☐	I'm in constant pain	☐	☐
I find it painful to change position	☐	☐	It takes me a long time to get to sleep	☐	☐
I feel lonely	☐	☐	I feel I am a burden to people	☐	☐

	Yes	No		Yes	No
I can only walk about indoors	☐	☐			
I find it hard to bend	☐	☐	Worry is keeping me awake at night	☐	☐
Everything is an effort	☐	☐	I feel that life is not worth living	☐	☐
			I sleep badly at night	☐	☐

	Yes	No		Yes	No
I'm waking up in the early hours of the morning	☐	☐			
I'm unable to walk at all	☐	☐	I'm finding it hard to get on with people	☐	☐
I'm finding it hard to make contact with people	☐	☐	I need help to walk about outside (eg, a walking aid or someone to support me)	☐	☐

	Yes	No		
The days seem to drag	☐	☐	I'm in pain when going up and down stairs or steps	☐ ☐
I have trouble getting up and down stairs or steps	☐	☐		
I find it hard to reach for things	☐	☐		

			Yes	No
		I wake up feeling depressed	☐	☐
		I'm in pain when I'm sitting	☐	☐

	Yes	No
I'm in pain when I walk	☐	☐
I lose my temper easily these days	☐	☐
I feel there is nobody I am close to	☐	☐

Part II

Now we would like you to think about the activities in your life which may be affected by health problems. In the list below, tick **Yes** for each activity in your life which is being affected by your state of health. Tick **No** for each activity which is not being affected, **or which does not apply to you**.

Is your present state of health causing problems with your . . .

	Yes	No			Yes	No
Job of work	☐	☐	Sex life		☐	☐
(That is, paid employment)						

Interests and hobbies ☐ ☐

Looking after the home ☐ ☐ (Examples: sports, arts and crafts,
(Examples: cleaning and cooking, do-it-yourself etc.)
repairs, odd jobs around the
home etc.) Holidays ☐ ☐
(Examples: summer or winter

Social life ☐ ☐ holidays, weekends away, etc.)
(Examples: going out, seeing
friends, going to the pub, etc.)

Home life ☐ ☐
(That is: relationships with other
people in your home)

REFERENCES

1 Culyer A J. Need values and health status measurement. In: Culyer A J and Wright K G (Eds). *Economic aspects of health services*, London, Martin Robertson, 1978, pp 9–31·

2 Martini C J M and McDowell I. Health status: patients and physician judgement. *Health Services Research, 11,* (4), 508–575 (1978).

3 McDowell I and Martini C J M, Problems and new directions in the evaluation of primary care. *International Journal of Epidemiology,* 5, 247–250 (1976).

4 McDowell I *et al.* A method for self-assessment of disability before and after hip replacement operations. *British Medical Journal,* 2, 875–879 (1978).

5 Hunt S M and McEwen J. The development of a subjective health indicator. *Sociology of Health and Illness,* 2, 231–246 (1980).

6 McKenna S P *et al.* Weighting the seriousness of perceived health problems using Thurstone's method of paired comparisons. *International Journal of Epidemiology, 10,* 93–97 (1981).

7 Hunt S M *et al.* A quantitative approach to perceived health status: a validation study. *Journal of Epidemiology and Community Health, 34,* 281–286 (1981).

8 Hunt S M *et al.* Nottingham profile: subjective health status and medical consultations. *Social Science and Medicine, 15a,* 221–29 (1981).

9 McKenna S P *et al.* Looking at health from the consumers point of view. *Occupational Health, 32,* 350–355 (1980).

10 McKenna S P *et al.* Absence from work and perceived health among mine rescue workers. *Journal of the Society of Occupational Medicine, 31,* 151–157 (1981).

11 Backett E M *et al. Health and quality of life.* Report to the Social Science Research Council, London, 1981.

The Nottingham health profile: a measure of perceived health 83

Health indicators in arthritis

Richard Brooks
University of Strathclyde

Introduction

There has been a major upsurge of interest recently concerning health indicators in arthritis. A significant number of articles investigating these indicators has appeared in the medical literature. In addition, two major conferences have been convened in the last 18 months, one at McMaster University, Canada (December 1981) and one in London (March 1983).

Arthritis is a term covering a variety of musculo-skeletal diseases which are regarded as chronic and, usually, disabling. Prominent among these diseases are rheumatoid arthritis, osteoarthritis, ankylosing spondylitis, systemic lupus erythematosus, gout and inflammatory polyarthritis. Arthritis is not primarily a matter of life and death but of deterioration over time of a sufferer's health. Control and, if possible, improvement of the arthritic patient's condition are therefore the primary aims of medical intervention.

The results of this intervention have to be assessed if only because medical personnel need some means of judging the 'success' or otherwise of their efforts. From the wider societal point of view we need to know whether the best use is being made of the resources devoted to arthritis care.

The chronic nature of arthritis and the attendant need for assessment of changes in patients' health states have generated various forms of health indicators to assess the nature and extent of arthritic disabilities and the outcomes of medical intervention. Liang and Jette cite Taylor in 1937 as one of the first to quantify function in individuals with arthritis and point out that in 1949 Steinbrocker's committee was the 'first to quantify functional status of the individual with arthritis in isolation from other disease-related variables'.[1, 2] The Steinbrocker classification (otherwise known as the American Rheumatism Association or ARA classification) has subsequently been extensively applied in arthritis assessment and is often used as a benchmark with which to compare new functional measures.[3]

From these early 'indicatorial' efforts has developed a whole battery of health indicators in arthritis. In addition, it has been pointed out that clinical rheumatologists were in the forefront in applying the methodology of controlled trials, a 1945 paper by Fraser being cited.[4, 5]

Objectives of health indicators

Any discussion of the 'usefulness', 'relevance' or otherwise of health indicators in arthritis ought to start with an exploration of the purposes for which we wish to develop these indicators. This issue can be addressed by viewing the possible interests of the different potential clients for such indicators.

The *patient's* main objective is to get better; he or she may be worried about the costs and side effects of treatments, about ability to do work or housework, or enjoy leisure or any one of the myriad aspects of 'social functioning'.

From the medical viewpoint, *doctors and other health personnel* are concerned with the assessment of the results of medical intervention. This can
be judged 'narrowly' through clinical investigation: here different indices
have different uses, are used at different levels of medical decision-making
and are intrinsically different. Thus for diagnosis, a diagnostic index is
required, for prognosis a prognostic index and to assess the efficacy of
treatment, a therapeutic index.[6] Medical personnel, then, will be very much
concerned with the 'clinical functioning' of the patient, with cure rates of
disease, with toxicity of drugs and so forth. They may also, in varying
degrees, pay attention to the socio-economic/psycho-social outcomes of
their activities. Similar criteria, particularly on the clinical side, will be of
interest to *drug companies, medical equipment suppliers* and the like.

The *health policy decision-maker's* main aim is to allocate scarce resources in
an optimal fashion, whether from the narrow viewpoint of, say, a hospital
administrator trying to make the best use of the financial resources available, or from the wider viewpoint, especially in a publicly-funded system, of
health service administrators attempting to optimize the use of society's
resources.

This cursory examination of the differing objectives, or at least
emphases, of medical intervention points up the likely need for different
health indicators to meet these different objectives.

As it happens, a wide range of indicators has traditionally been used for
clinical assessment and judgement in arthritis; functional assessment has
received detailed study and, more recently, considerable attention has been
devoted to the development of indicators which attempt to meet the need
for the broader, psycho-socio-economic measurement of medical intervention in arthritis.

Arthritis indicators
There are two broad areas of arthritis indicators:
1) 'rheumatology standards',
2) health status or health evaluation indicators.

1 *Rheumatology standards*
A comprehensive list of 20 such indicators was presented at the McMaster
conference (see Table 1).[7] All of these measures have been used in clinical
trials in arthritis. Amongst those attending the conference the most popular measures were joint count, pain and global scores, which accounted for
60 per cent of the total score for all measures, with a further 30 per cent
accounted for by morning stiffness, grip strength, time to walk, joint swell-
ings and ESR.

Some of these are characterized as 'process' indicators and can be distinguished from outcome measures, which have been developed as health
status and health evaluation indicators.

2 *Health status and health evaluation indicators*
(i) *Functional (or health status) indicators*
As noted in the Introduction, the first of these was the ARA instrument for
standardizing functional capacity (see Table 2). Following the recognition of
the need for outcome measures a series of functional indicators emerged,
many of which contained criteria for 'activities of daily living' (ADL). Typi-

TABLE 1 **Rheumatology standards**

1 Joint count
2 Patient-rated measure of pain relief
3 Global assessment of change in disease activity
4 Patient-rated measure of pain
5 Global assessment of change in disease activity
6 Duration of morning stiffness
7 Grip strength
8 Time to walk 50 feet
9 Joint swelling
10 ESR
11 Analgesic consumption
12 Time until onset of fatigue
13 Tenderness measured by instrument
14 Haemoglobin
15 Weight loss
16 Thermography
17 X-Ray
18 Rheumatoid factor
19 Technetium^{99} uptake
20 Xenon^{133} clearance

Source Bombadier C, Tugwell P, Sinclair A, *et al*, 'Preference for endpoint measures in clinical trials: results of structured workshops,' *Journal of Rheumatology* 9: 798–801, 1982.

cally, questions were asked of patients about self-care (dressing, bathing, feeding, etc) and about mobility. Twelve of these functional assessment measures (including ARA) were critically reviewed by Liang and Jette.[1]

ii) *Health evaluation indicators*

The latter authors and other researchers felt unhappy with all these functional indices on a variety of methodological grounds. There are some differences in scope and emphasis amongst different authors, but nevertheless a wide measure of agreement on what standards should be met by any index purporting to be a health status or evaluation measure. The drive for methodological 'soundness' has meant that all the more recent indices proposed in arthritis assessment have been tested in varying measure by their proponents.

What are these methodological criteria? In reviewing the literature the present author found the following on offer: quantifiability, reliability, validity (content, face, criterion, discriminant, construct, predictive), precision, simplicity, generalizability, sensitivity, economy (ease of performance), objectivity (inter-observer agreement), practicality (costs, time to collect data, questions comprehensible), usefulness (for patient management, resource allocation). In addition some attention has been paid

TABLE 2 **ARA functional classification**

I complete ability to carry on all usual duties without handicaps
II adequate for normal activities, despite handicap of discomfort or limited motion at one or more joints
III limited only to little or none of duties of usual occupation or self-care
IV incapacitated largely or wholly, bed-ridden, or confined to wheelchair; little or no self-care

Source Bombardier C, Tugwell P, Sinclair A, *et al*, 'Preference for endpoint measures in clinical trials: results of structured workshops,' *Journal of Rheumatology* 9: 798–801, 1982.

to specification of data collection procedures, administration (interview, self-assessment, clinical judgement), and type of scale used (ordinal, cardinal). These are clearly not mutually exclusive criteria, eg sensitivity is similar to discriminant validity; simplicity, economy, and practicality are closely related and so on. Most investigators are, however, agreed that indicators should meet reliability, validity, generalizability, sensitivity and objectivity tests.

In arthritis at least 5 health evaluation indicators are 'on the market'. These are:

Arthritis Impact Measurement Scales (AIMS)[8, 9, 10]
Health Assessment Questionnaire (HAQ)[11, 12, 13]
McMaster Health Index Questionnaire (MHIQ)[14]
Sickness Impact Profile (SIP)[15, 16]
Toronto Questionnaire (TQ)[17]

Some details of these instruments are shown in Tables 3–7.

All these indicators have, as noted above, been subjected to methodological tests by the respective investigators, but as yet detailed independent observer critiques are lacking. (See, however, Jette for some comments on earlier reports of the SIP.)[18] Little cross-testing of the measures has been attempted, with the exception of the results reported in Liang et al.[19] The AIMS and HAQ have also been tested for cross-validity.[12] On the whole, most of the investigators are satisfied with the methodological soundness of their own measures and are keen to explore the potential uses for decision-making of these measures.

Discussion

To an economist seeking to assess changes in personal (patient) 'utility' and societal 'welfare' the health evaluation indicators recently developed in arthritis are a disappointment. Although it could be argued that *any* instrument capable of detecting changes in health status at the individual level

TABLE 3 **Sickness impact profile (SIP)**

12 categories	number of questions
Ambulation	12
Mobility	10
Body care } Movement }	23
Social interaction	20
Communication	9
Emotional behaviour	9
Alertness behaviour	10
Eating	9
Work	9
Sleep and rest	7
Household management	10
Recreation and pastimes	8
	136

Source Deyo R A, Inui T S, Leininger J, Overman S, 'Physical and psychosocial function in rheumatoid arthritis. Clinical use of a self-administered instrument,' *Archives of Internal Medicine* 142: 879–82, 1982.

TABLE 4 **McMaster Health Index Questionnaire (MHIQ)**

3 indices	number of questions
Physical function	19
Emotional function	25
Social function	25
	69

Source Chambers L W, MacDonald L A, Tugwell P, *et al*, 'The McMaster Health Index Questionnaire as a measure of quality of life for patients with rheumatoid disease,' *Journal of Rheumatology* 9: 780–84, 1982.

TABLE 5 **Toronto Questionnaire**

4 dimensions	number of questions
Mobility	17
Personal care	22
Hand and arm function	7
Work/play activity	10
	56

Source Helewa A, Goldsmith C H, Smythe H A, 'Independent measurement of functional capacity in rheumatoid arthritis,' *Journal of Rheumatology* 9: 794–97, 1982.

TABLE 6 **Arthritis Impact Measurement Scales (AIMS)**

9 component scales	number of questions
Mobility	4
Physical activity	5
Dexterity	5
Household activities	7
Activities of daily living	4
Anxiety	6
Depression	6
Social activity	4
Pain	4
	45

Sources Meenan R F, Gertman P M, Mason J H, 'Measuring health status in arthritis: the arthritis impact measurement scales,' *Arthritis and Rheumatism* 23: 146–52, 1980.
Meenan R F, 'The AIMS approach to health status measurement: conceptual background and measurement properties,' *Journal of Rheumatology* 9: 785–88, 1982.

TABLE 7 **Health Assessment Questionnaire (HAQ)**

8 components	number of questions
Dressing/grooming	2
Arising	2
Eating	3
Walking	2
Hygiene	3
Reach	2
Grip	3
Activities	3
	20

Source Fries J F, Spitz P W, Young D Y, 'The dimensions of health outcomes: the health assessment questionnaire, disability and pain scales,' *Journal of Rheumatology* 9: 789–93, 1982.

and, especially, capable of aggregating such changes across individuals, would provide 'outcome' measures useful in, eg cost-effectiveness or cost-benefit analysis, the indicators on offer at present do not look too promising in this regard.

Most of the arthritis evaluation measures contain variables which might be said to have economic content. Little explicit regard is paid, however, in the publications reporting these measures, to the economic dimensions of resource use in arthritis care and control. One major exception is the HAQ measure, one of whose dimensions is 'economic impact'[20] and Fries' paper[13] contains some economic discussion, even to the extent of mentioning the possible need for discounting of future events, a matter largely ignored in the arthritis literature. It should be noted also that the American Rheumatism Association includes 21 items under the head Socioeconomic Status as part of its 'Uniform Database' for rheumatic disease.[21]

Little attention, also, has been paid in the arthritis health evaluation literature to the question of linking cost with outcomes: it seems to be implicitly assumed that as long as improvements in function or health status are shown from medical intervention, then resources will (ought to be?) found to generate these improvements.

Now perhaps these criticisms are unfair in the sense that much of the work undertaken so far has had the limited aim of generating outcome measures for the assessment of clinical trials: thus any movement from process measures to outcome measures ought to be welcomed. There is some scepticism in medical circles, however, concerning the usefulness of the health evaluation indicators on offer even on these rather narrow grounds. The rheumatology standards were alleged to have little impact on physician behaviour and the emotional and social scales proposed in the health evaluation indicators were thought not to be of use in discriminating between effective and ineffective therapy.[22]

The sensitivity of the various indicators to clinically meaningful changes has been called into question.[19] If it is difficult to discriminate at the level of the individual it almost certainly follows that the problems of aggregation to obtain social valuations of health status changes are formidable.

A further important criticism of the evaluation techniques developed so far is that, perhaps paradoxically, the patient tends to be ignored, in the sense that his or her wishes, values, preferences and expectations are not often explicitly incorporated in the evaluation instruments.[22, 23] To an economist this is a pity: one of the more promising developments in the evaluation of health care has been the exploration of ways of measuring willingness-to-pay (WTP) on the part of actual or potential consumers of health care resources. This approach is addressed to individual preferences valued explicitly in money terms: this should not be anathema where scarce resources are involved. At least one attempt has, in fact, been made to assess WTP in arthritis.[24] The basic question of whose values should 'count' in any evaluation is a fundamental one and does require considerable exploration of the value premises upon which evaluation instruments are constructed[13, 19] Little attention is paid to this issue in the arthritis work.

One further criticism before a more constructive note will be struck: there is a very real worry that instruments developed within one medico-socio-economic framework, eg that of the United States, will not be applicable in other cultures, eg the United Kingdom. This does not matter when patients answer questions about ability to dress, walk, grip, etc, but it may well do so when the wider social and economic variables are under consideration. This issue may also be relevant when patient behaviour in the very different *medical* settings is under investigation. Detailed arthritis health evaluation indicators have not been separately developed in the UK, although a number of the functional/health status indices did emanate from the UK (see eg[25]). Much of the British work has concentrated on measuring functional disability (for a recent example see[26]). One study has applied the HAQ in the British setting: the results seem to indicate its applicability in this country.[27] In addition the SIP was modified by Patrick for use in Britain and emerged as the Functional Limitation Profile (FLP).[28]

So much for critical comment; what other issues can be raised? First, there is plenty of sound advice contained in the literature about the necessary requirements for methodologically sound clinical trial and health evaluation instruments (see eg,[6, 13, 19, 29]). Perhaps the soundest advice of all comes from Meenan,[10] who has suggested that designers of new outcome (evaluation) instruments in arthritis might well be advised to desist! So choice from the present instruments available, with due modification for the circumstances investigators find themselves in, may be the most cost-effective way of proceeding. Remembering, however, the 'cross-cultural translation' difficulty just noted, it is likely still to be necessary to develop appropriate instruments for the UK setting.

Second, whilst most of the evaluation indicators on offer are primarily cross-sectional in nature, they do appear to be capable of adaptation for longitudinal studies, a factor of crucial importance in arthritis evaluation. Indeed, it has been suggested that the rheumatology standards are most appropriate for short-term assessment, whilst the evaluation indicators will prove more useful for extended studies.[22]

Third, the constructive suggestion has been made that clinician and methodologist should grow together so that interaction between the two might produce indicators which are capable of meeting the needs of medical personnel for criteria to help them judge the consequences of their activities.[4] To which one would be willing to agree, with the proviso that economists be regarded as methodologists in this regard!

The latter statement is of course special pleading, but it is not necessary to apologize for this. The work that has so far been undertaken on health indicators in arthritis seems to be some distance removed from the conceptual framework (specifically: cost-effectiveness, cost-benefit analysis) that economists are familiar with. The sooner work is done to integrate the two approaches, the sooner will there be a framework available which ought to help decision-makers reach informed judgements about appropriate uses of the scarce resources that society may care to devote to the care of those suffering from arthritis.

REFERENCES

1 Liang M H, Jette A M, 'Measuring functional ability in arthritis.' *Arthritis and Rheumatism* 24: 80–86, 1981.

2 Taylor D, 'A table for the degree of involvement in chronic arthritis,' *Canadian Medical Association J* 36:608–10, 1937.

3 Steinbrocker O, Traeger C H, Battman R C, 'Therapeutic criteria in rheumatoid arthritis,' *Journal of the American Medical Association* 140: 659–62, 1949.

4 Buchanan W W, Smythe H A, 'Can clinicians and statisticians be friends?' *Journal of Rheumatology* 9: 653–54, 1982.

5 Fraser T N, 'Gold treatment in rheumatoid arthritis,' *Annals of the Rheumatic Diseases* 4: 71–75, 1945.

6 Bombardier C, Tugwell P, 'A methodological framework to develop and select indices for clinical trials: statistical and judgemental approaches,' *Journal of Rheumatology* 9: 793–57, 1982.

7 Bombardier C, Tugwell P, Sinclair A, *et al*, 'Preference for endpoint measures in clinical trials: results of structured workshops,' *Journal of Rheumatology* 9: 798–801, 1982.

8 Meenan R F, Gertman P M, Mason J H, 'Measuring health status in arthritis: the arthritis impact measurement scales,' *Arthritis and Rheumatism* 23: 146–52, 1980.

9 Meenan R F, Gertman P M, Mason J H, Dunaif R, 'The arthritis impact measurement scales: further investigations of a health status measure,' *Arthritis and Rheumatism* 25: 1048–53, 1982.

10 Meenan R F, 'The AIMS approach to health status measurement: conceptual background and measurement properties,' *Journal of Rheumatology* 9: 785–88, 1982.

11 Fries J F, Spitz P, Kraines R G, Holman H R, 'Measurement of patient outcome in arthritis,' *Arthritis and Rheumatism* 23: 137–45, 1980.

12 Fries J F, Spitz P W, Young D Y, 'The dimensions of health outcomes: the health assessment questionnaire, disability and pain scales,' *Journal of Rheumatology* 9: 789–93, 1982.

13 Fries J F, 'The assessment of disability: from first to future principles,' paper presented at the conference *Advances in Assessing Arthritis* at The London Hospital, March 1983, (mimeo).

14 Chambers L W, MacDonald L A, Tugwell P, *et al*, 'The McMaster Health Index Questionnaire as a measure of quality of life for patients with rheumatoid disease,' *Journal of Rheumatology* 9: 780–84, 1982.

15 Deyo R A, Inui T S, Leininger J, Overman S, 'Physical and psychosocial function in rheumatoid arthritis. Clinical use of a self-administered instrument,' *Archives of Internal Medicine* 142: 879–82, 1982.

16 Deyo R A, Inui T S, Leininger J D, Overman S S, 'Measuring functional status in chronic disease: a comparison of traditional scales and a self-administered health status questionnaire in patients with rheumatoid arthritis,' *Medical Care* 21: 180–92, 1983.

17 Helewa A, Goldsmith C H, Smythe H A, 'Independent measurement of functional capacity in rheumatoid arthritis,' *Journal of Rheumatology* 9: 794–97, 1982.

18 Jette A M, 'Health status indicators: their utility in chronic disease evaluation research,' *Journal of Chronic Diseases* 33: 567–79, 1980.

19 Liang M H, Cullen K, Larson M, 'In search of a more perfect mousetrap (health status or quality of life instrument)', *Journal of Rheumatology* 9: 775–79, 1982.

20 Lubeck D P, Spitz P W, Fries J F, 'The health assessment questionnaire (HAQ): Assessment of personal economic costs,' *Arthritis and Rheumatism* 25:s 149, 1982.

21 Fries J F, Hess E V, Klinenberg J R, 'A uniform database for rheumatic disease,' *Arthritis and Rheumatism* 22: 1029–33, 1979.

22 Decker J L, 'Summary of conference on outcome measurement in rheumatology clinical trials,' *Journal of Rheumatology* 9: 802–6, 1982.

23 Burton K E, Wright V, 'Functional assessment,' paper presented to the conference *Advances in Assessing Arthritis* at The London Hospital, March 1983, (mimeo).

24 Thompson M S, Read J L, Liang M, 'Willingness-to-pay concepts for societal decisions in health,' in *Values and Long-Term Care,* Kane R L and Kane R A (eds), Lexington, 1982.

25 Lee P, Jasani M K, Dick W C, Buchanan W W, 'Evaluation of a functional index in rheumatoid arthritis,' *Scandinavian Journal of Rheumatology* 2: 71–77, 1973.

26 Wagstaff S, Badley E M, Wood P H N, 'Interrelationship between functional limitation (impairment) and activity restriction (disability) in patients with rheumatoid arthritis,' *International Journal of Rehabilitation Research* 4: 293–94, 1981.

27 Kirwan J R, Reeback J S, 'Using a modified Stanford Health Assessment Questionnaire to assess disability in UK patients with rheumatoid arthritis,' *Annals of the Rheumatic Diseases* 42: 219–20, 1983.

28 Patrick D (ed), *The Longitudinal Disability Interview Survey: Phase I Report*, Social Medicine and Health Services Research Unit, St Thomas's Hospital Medical School, London, 1981.
29 Tugwell P, Bombardier C, 'A methodologic framework for developing and selecting end-points in clinical trials,' *Journal of Rheumatology* 9: 758–62, 1982.

Measurement of benefits in the treatment of arthritis

Edward Huskisson
St Bartholomew's Hospital, London

Introduction

Rheumatologists have done well in the development of measures of symptoms and signs in arthritis. They have done less well in measuring aspects of their disease processes, many of which are of unknown aetiology. They may envy the high technology of their cardiological colleagues but have progressed beyond the use of trinitrin tablet counting to measure angina. They have avoided the error of measuring peak flow in asthma instead of breathlessness. They have many problems including the variability of their patients and the end-points of their diseases. They may admire those interested in hypertension who have studied the effects of treatment on a very clear-cut outcome, stroke, but have come to recognise the importance of starting to study the outcome of arthritis. This must be added to an already long list of available measures which need further refinement.

Two fundamental principles

Measurements, I wish to suggest, arise or are developed in response to the desire to document a treatment effect. Existing measurements will therefore show the actions of currently available treatments. Analgesics relieve pain, which can be measured. Anti-inflammatory drugs relieve pain but do much more. They also reduce stiffness, swelling and tenderness, which can be measured. Penicillamine-like drugs do more still: as well as improving pain and inflammation, they reduce ESR and rheumatoid factor titre in rheumatoid arthritis; they may improve extra-articular features and perhaps slow down the progression of X-ray changes and improve the outcome of the disease. Penicillamine-like drugs have a disease-dependent action. Similarly allopurinol is effective only in gout, controlling the serum uric acid as well as the clinical manifestations of the disease. For many diseases like osteoarthritis, there is no specific therapy. Perhaps it is the paucity of treatments which alter outcome that has limited the development of measures to demonstrate such an effect.

The choice of measurement will always be determined by the aims of the experiment. Experiments designed to show the pain-relieving or uric acid-lowering effects of a drug must measure pain relief or uric acid. There has been a tendency in rheumatology to make a large number of measurements of the disease in the hope of finding something which improves. It is undesirable for statistical reasons to make multiple measurements especially when the parameters are related. We should therefore look carefully at the measures which we have and decide which ones we need.

Measurement of symptoms and signs

A lot of trouble in joints is caused by inflammation, the cardinal signs of which form the basis of many measurements. Pain is very important. It is the major reason why patients complain and why they seek treatment. It can be measured. Keele introduced a simple descriptive scale, grading pain as severe, moderate, mild or absent and showed that this could be used to document the action of a narcotic analgesic.[1] A visual analogue scale is often preferred because it is more sensitive to change.[2] Various other methods have been suggested. Morning stiffness is another important symptom in inflammatory arthritis. It is reduced by anti-inflammatory drugs and its duration can be measured by the patient. The tenderness of joints is the basis for joint counts and articular indices such as that of Ritchie *et al*[3]. It is surprisingly difficult to measure swelling. There is a device developed from jewellers' rings to measure the circumference of the proximal interphalangeal joints. The circumference of other joints like the knee is not a useful measure because an enormous change in volume is required to make a significant change in circumference. Knee joint volume can be measured by xeroradiography.[4] Warmth can be measured by infra-red thermography but like isotopic measurements, complex apparatus is required and does not usually justify the information gained. One could never say that a patient was better because the thermographic or isotopic index had improved. Measures of functional impairment are considered below.

Measurements of the disease process

In rheumatoid arthritis, some guide to the activity and severity of the disease is provided by ESR and rheumatoid factor titre. Though changes in these measures are a marker of the action of drugs like penicillamine, they correlate poorly with improvement in pain and other clinical measures. X-rays are currently the only method which has been used to show changes in the outcome of the disease. Various drugs including gold, penicillamine and immunosuppressives have been shown to retard the progression of X-ray changes in some studies. This may not be a good measure of outcome since there is no evidence that erosive disease is related to the development of deformities or functional impairment. X-ray appearance in rheumatoid arthritis is also influenced by other factors such as physical activity. The time has come to develop better measures of outcome which will reflect those aspects of the disease that concern both patient and physician.

Functional measurements

There is increasing interest in measures of function in arthritis. There are many methods. Steinbrocker *et al* introduced a simple descriptive scale but like the corresponding pain scale, it lacks sensitivity to change.[5] Visual analogue scales have been used on the assumption that disability is subjective.[6] The use of these scales showed that there was a poor correlation between a patient's assessment of his disability and assessment by an observer or the time taken to achieve a particular task. It also became clear that no single function could be used in a group of patients with rheumatoid arthritis. While most patients have pain, one has bad hands and can't write while another has bad knees and can't walk. The best guide to the benefit of treatment with penicillamine-like drugs was therefore a visual analogue scale measuring a particular function chosen by the patient as his biggest problem. A global assessment of function was less efficient and a measure of one standard function was of little value. Lee *et al* devised an index based on activities of daily living and showed that it was sensitive to treatment.[7] The current fashion is questionnaires such as the Stanford Health Assessment Questionnaire of Fries *et al.*[8] These are discussed in the proceedings of a conference on outcome measures in rheumatological clinical trials.[9] They have not been shown to be responsive to treatment. They may hide the problem of variability but it exists with all these methods. Is it valid to compare improvement in the man who can't walk and the woman who can't write? It is probably no less valid than to compare their pains, but it is a problem to be recognised and remembered.

Another approach to function is tests such as grip strength and walking time. Their major limitation is surely the small amount of information achieved. Grip strength tells you how much a patient can and will squeeze a bag on a particular day. Grip and walking ability may not be the patients' problems and may not reflect the aims of treatment in a particular patient.

Outcome measurements

There are many things that happen to patients with arthritis. They may die but seldom because of arthritis. They may require an operation, develop deformities or restriction of movement, require social security, become dependent on others or even go into remission. They may or may not continue to take their tablets and this has been used as a measure of the value of non-steroidal anti-inflammatory drugs. They may develop side effects. In an early penicillamine study, Huskisson and Hart noted that a number of patients returned to work.[10] These outcomes concern both patients and physician and need to be measured. But it is difficult. A successful outcome may be quite different for a housewife, a builders' labourer, a retired man and a schoolgirl. It would be nice to find some common measure like money to overcome this variability but it has not so far been achieved. Any method which is developed will be tested in the harsh world of clinical trials and must give the right answers as well as being reliable, sensitive, valid and reproducible. Synovectomy was judged a success by cost-benefit analysis but controlled trials and subsequent experience judged the operation a failure and it has been abandoned.

Conclusions

Many benefits of anti-rheumatic drugs can be demonstrated including relief of pain and stiffness, improvement in aspects of some disease processes and better function. It can be argued that we have no drugs which do more. We need to know more about the outcome of our diseases and to develop measurements capable of showing changes in outcome.

We should look to reducing the number of measurements which we make. Those which we choose should be simple, responsive and directed at those aspects of the disease which are the objective of treatment. We should distrust complicated indices which often tell us nothing. We do not want to know whether a drug changed an index; we want to know whether it relieved pain or altered the outcome of the disease. I suspect that when we can alter the outcome of the diseases we treat, we shall want to see the benefits in simple terms, counting the number of patients who have returned to work, developed deformities or required surgery. The solution to variability is larger numbers of patients studied rather than indices to make small numbers look alike.

REFERENCES

1 Keele K D. 'The pain chart'. *Lancet* 1948; 2: 6–8.
2 Huskisson E C. 'Measurement of pain'. *Lancet* 1974; 2: 1127–31.
3 Ritchie D M, Boyle J A, McInnes J M, Jasami M K, Dalakos T G, Grieveson P and Buchanan W W. 'Clinical studies with an articular index for the assessment of joint tenderness in patients with rheumatoid arthritis'. *Quarterly Journal of Medicine*, 1968; 37: 393–406.
4 Gumpel J M, Matthews S A, Altman D G, Spencer J D and Wilkins E A. 'An objective assessment of synovitis of the knee: measurement of the size of the suprapatellar pouch on xeroradiography'. *Annals of Rheumatic Diseases* 1980; 39: 359–66.
5 Steinbrocker O, Traeger C H, Batterman R C. 'Therapeutic criteria in rheumatoid arthritis'. *Journal of the American Medical Association* 1949; 140: 659–62.
6 Scott P J and Huskisson E C. 'Measurement of functional capacity with visual analogue scales'. *Rheumatism and Rehabilitation* 1977; 16: 257–9.
7 Lee P, Jasani M K, Dick W C, Buchanan W W. 'Evaluation of a functional index in rheumatoid arthritis'. *Scandiavian Journal of Rheumatology* 1973; 2: 71–7.
8 Fries J F, Spitz P W, Kraines R G and Holman H R. 'Measurement of patient outcome in arthritis'. *Arthritis and Rheumatism* 1980; 23: 137–45.
9 'Proceedings of the conference on outcome measures in rheumatological clinical trials'. *Journal of Rheumatology* 1982; 9: 753–806.
10 Huskisson E C and Hart F D. 'Penicillamine in the treatment of rheumatoid arthritis'. *Annals of Rheumatic Diseases* 1972; 31: 402–4.

Measuring the socio-economic benefits of auranofin

Morton Paterson

SK&F Laboratories, Philadelphia

Evaluation framework

I would like to lead up to auranofin and Smith Kline & French's efforts to measure its broader benefits by referring to 'Tagamet'. 'Tagamet' came first and, being a *relatively* simple case, taught us to plan a cost-benefit approach.

The first thing we did to study the broader benefits of 'Tagamet' was to put a simple, one-line item in the case report form of an early six-week US trial in acute duodenal ulcer: 'Days of work missed last week.' That's about all the gastroenterologists could take time to ask. About the same time in Sweden, investigators in Linköping put a similar item in their year-long trial of 'Tagamet'. They also kept track of who had to have surgery. We found the 'Tagamet' patients missed much less work and had far fewer ulcer operations than did the placebo controls. The focus of these studies is the clinical trial, in these instances randomised and double blind. At the pre-approval stage of a drug, the clinical trial presents a fleeting opportunity to apply broader measures of drug effect under the rigorous and respected conditions of a randomised double-blind experiment. Scientific respectability seems especially important when you try to introduce newer, broader and some would say 'softer' measures of outcome than the hard data regulatory authorities usually want – ulcers healed on endoscopy, numbers of swollen joints, and so on.

Another type of study we did was 'forecasts', estimates by clinical investigators and others, of how 'Tagamet' would affect various ulcer patients' treatment and response patterns: concomitant drugs used, office visits, hospitalisations, surgery, disability and death. We compared these responses against estimates for traditionally-treated patients, costed out the percentage differences, and applied them to national costs of ulcer disease. The national costs had been determined in a previous cost-of-disease study by an outside research organisation. All this gave us projections, no hard data, but was useful in identifying where the cost savings might occur.

Next, after 'Tagamet' was introduced, we watched time series statistics on hospitalisation, surgery, work loss, and so on in any relevant data base we could find – government health care surveys, state Medicaid data, centralised health data in European countries, to name a few. This put us heavily into epidemiology, where indeed we have to be if we want to see if the promises from the randomised trials come true in the real world of the community. 'Tagamet' taught us a few things here that will be relevant to auranofin. One is that you have to wait for the time series to run. Two years do not a trend make. Second, it often takes another year or longer for the government or other agencies to collect and publish the data you want. Third, you need a rapidly and widely accepted drug like 'Tagamet' if you want to see any effect on much of the trend data. And fourth, even if you see a clear trend break in the statistics – like a sharp drop in ulcer surgery – people will be most happy to suggest other reasons for it than the drug in question. As they should: *Post hoc non ergo proper hoc.* Hence, fifth, we had to confirm the trend phenomena in different countries.

A parallel approach used after marketing was to track the utilisation of services of 'Tagamet'-treated ulcer patients versus that of all other ulcer patients, that is those patients treated traditionally. The problem here is selection bias. Unlike clinical trials, patients are not assigned at random. Actually, the more serious cases got 'Tagamet', at least initially. So the comparison is unfair and you have to resort to regression analysis and all its complex adjustments to try to start the two groups out equal.

Finally, as another approach, we encouraged decision-tree studies. If you know the medical outcome probabilities from clinical trials and have related treatment patterns to choose from – 'Tagamet' versus surgery, for example – you can apply their outcome probabilities to the costs of the outcomes and get an expected value for the costs of the alternative treatments. Alan Maynard has referred to his excellent study of this type.

Now, let me restate these 'Tagamet' approaches as a general framework in which our auranofin efforts can be situated. More or less chronologically we have these sources of benefit information:
1 Pre-marketing clinical trials, hopefully randomised and double-blind
2 Cost of disease studies, apart from the drug in question
3 Estimates of future drug effect on these costs
4 Decision-tree probability costings of alternative treatments and
5 Epidemiologic studies after marketing in the community:
   – time-series studies or
   – cross-sectional type studies, in which patients who get the drug are compared with those who do not – with an attempt to control biases of patient selection.
Where does auranofin fit in here?

As we looked back at 'Tagamet' and forward to auranofin, it seemed ever more important to learn everything we could at the pre-marketing, clinical trial phase. There are a number of reasons for this. First of all, we were interested in quality of life, not just costs. I was happy to learn from our 'Tagamet' projects that economics is not just costs, as many people think, but also what utility or satisfaction you get for those costs. Thus, cost-benefits studies must be quite serious about benefits, even if you can't put dollar values on them.

Any therapeutic benefits of auranofin mentioned today are hypothetical and for methodology purposes. I am not reporting actual efficacy or safety findings of any clinical study.

An auranofin hypothesis
Auranofin is the first oral form of gold. Injectable gold has long been used for rheumatoid arthritis, usually after other agents have been tried. It is one of the so-called remission inducing or disease modifying agents, aimed at the disease mechanism itself. Gold does not relieve the pain of joint inflammation *per se*, as non-steroidal anti-inflammatories do – your Brufens and Feldenes. Gold usually takes weeks or months to reach full effect. Gold injections are once a week. The auranofin dosage is two tablets a day.

Patients in whom auranofin replaces injectable gold will experience *at the least* the benefits of not being stuck with a needle every week and of avoiding the inconvenience of the doctor visit necessary for that injection. Treatment or monitoring costs will probably be less than with injectable gold. In fact, treatment costs can essentially be calculated and compared on paper: number of visits, costs of injections, costs of tablets, frequency and cost of tests, and so on. Given that favourable cost outcome, why bother about measuring the benefits of convenience and less injection pain? Actually, it is in patients *not* getting injectable gold but who are *candidates for oral gold* that the measure of benefits is more important. In these patients auranofin will be add-on therapy. Non-steroidal anti-inflammatories will be continued for pain, at least for some time. Thus, it is possible that total treatment costs for these patients will be increased, at least in the near term, before they decline. If costs are increased, it is all the more important to measure the benefits obtained for those costs. It is important from at least two points of view. Firstly, rheumatologists have for some time now wanted more meaningful, objective, outcome-oriented measures of efficacy – or benefit – for anti-rheumatic drugs and therapy. And second, health care insurers, reimbursers, administrators, and policy makers want to know nowadays whether new therapies are cost effective. At the accounting level, do they reduce treatment costs? If not, do they produce more health benefits for patients for their added costs? As everyone here knows, authorities are asking this kind of question more and more often as a way to control the costs of health care. With all this in mind, the pre-marketing, clinical trial phase seemed to be an important time to seize.

Let me elaborate. First of all, when else can you measure the effect of a drug on the patient's quality of life? After the drug is marketed, statistics may perhaps be kept on the number of office visits for rheumatoid arthritis, the number of hospitalisations, joint operations, hip replacements, and lost workdays, for instance. But no government or hospital statistics are likely to be kept on the pain, the mobility, the social interaction, and the psychological state of the auranofin patient. Certainly none would normally be kept on a comparable group of non-auranofin patients. Quality of life must be measured as it happens. Secondly, the randomised clinical trial allows you to get at cause and effect in a 'clean' way. If we were going to try to measure changes in quality of life – involving outcomes new to many physicians – we did not want to do so in an open, unrandomised trial and then have the whole new effort impugned as unscientific. Put another way, we did not find prestigious rheumatologists with an interest in quality-of-life measures who wanted to help us plan a clinical trial that was not randomised and double-blind. And rightly so, I think, since the disease varies normally over time and patients are amenable to all kinds of suggestion and placebo-type influences. We needed a control group. After marketing, with the drug available to all, it is difficult – even unethical some would say – to repeat a trial in which half the patients are successfully kept off the effective agent. Therefore, we were, again, locked into the pre-marketing, clinical trial phase.

Another reason we felt the pre-marketing phase was an important time to work in was the small chance of seeing an effect of auranofin in the post-marketing statistics routinely collected by health authorities. 'Tagamet' was unique. It worked promptly in acute episodes of an easily definable disease and so was rapidly and widely accepted. It was used in most countries in over 50 per cent of ulcer patient visits within a year of market introduction. Before 'Tagamet', hospitalisation and major surgery occurred as an end-point in a fairly large percentage of patients, so that improved ulcer healing might be expected to reduce that percentage and with it a large share of treatment costs. Also, very importantly, no other major innovations or shifts in therapy occurred at the same time. However, even if auranofin were soon used in 50 per cent of rheumatoid arthritis patients, I'm not sure what statistical index would be affected in a clear-cut way. Surgery in RA is less common than in ulcer. With the slow evolution of the arthritic process itself, I doubt we should count on seeing any sudden drop in the number of hip replacements or other joint surgery. And if a gradual drop occurs in the trend, then other drugs or new practices may claim causality. Again, the prospective controlled trial avoids this problem.

So, I now want to go into the theoretical and practical implications of executing a goal which may be stated thus: In a randomised, double-blind, clinical trial measure the effect of auranofin on quality of life and, as far as possible, on the cost of disease, and relate the two economically.

First, the theory: How do we relate costs and benefits? The cost-benefit model says the value of auranofin equals its benefits minus its costs: $V = B - C$. We would need to enumerate all the intangible benefits auranofin may provide — the improved function, the reduced pain, the better self-image and attitude — in effect all of what we mean by quality of life, with the negative of side effects subtracted out. At the same time, we would need to find the net costs of auranofin: that is, higher drug costs and patient visit costs, perhaps, minus lower steroid injection and physical therapy costs, perhaps, giving the net effect on cost of the disease. These we could hope to figure out in dollars or kronor or pounds; and we could even hope to cost out the absenteeism avoided and the disability retirements post-poned, so as to include indirect costs in the *net* cost of the disease. But now we come to the problem that the equation calls for us to subtract the net costs *from* the net quality-of-life benefits. So the benefit must also be expressed in money! How do you value a pain free day or the ability to dress yourself or play golf in dollars? Let me explain why this is theoreti-cally necessary. What we want to know is whether the benefits of using auranofin exceed the costs of using it. The value of using it, V equals $B - C$, net benefits minus net cost.

Let us pretend the value of ulcer treatment before 'Tagamet' could be expressed as 10: benefit of treatment of 15 minus cost of 5. We *could* increase the 10 to 12 just by decreasing the costs to 3: 15 minus $3 = 12$. The benefit was assumed constant at 15. If we assume the benefit, whatever it is, stays at least the same, we don't have to express it in dollars or even as a number. The gain in value comes from reducing the net costs. This is why the cost-reducing effect of 'Tagamet', in and of itself, may produce an improved. cost-benefit relationship. That's why, with hindsight, we were able to proceed without studying the quality-of-life effects of 'Tagamet'. Look now in rheumatoid arthritis what happens with auranofin if benefits are assumed the same but costs increase. With benefits still at 15 and costs at 7, say, value goes down to 8. If costs go up, we cannot rely on an assumption of unchanged benefits. We must measure them and see if they increase. The true equation may well be V equals benefits of 20 minus costs of 7 or a value of 13 – a *net gain* in value of 3 over previous or alternate therapy. But, as I said, we don't know how to express the quality-of-life benefits in dollars. What to do? The answer is, we shift to a different expression of economic value: cost-effectiveness, a less ambitious version of cost-benefit. In cost-effectiveness, we don't try to measure the benefits in money. We express them in an added unit of some good or desirable outcome – joints moveable, pain free days, trips out of the house, returns to work, social interactions, and so forth. The relationship becomes a ratio: for example, pain free days per dollar of net treatment cost. Say that one day costs $5, or 1 PFD over $5. Note that the ratio by itself doesn't mean anything. Is it a high ratio or a low one? In cost-effectiveness we have to also have a ratio for an alternative or comparison therapy. Thus, if the ratio for auranofin is a pain free day per $5 and for the alternative it is a pain free day per $7, auranofin is more cost-effective, at least by this measure of outcome. But what if by another measure of outcome – say days out of bed – auranofin is less effective? We need a unit of outcome encompassing and relating all or most of the aspects of the disease in question. Health economists want a unit that also allows comparison of cost-effectiveness of treating one condition versus that of treating another. This will allow rational allocation of monies in a health programme budget where they will do the most good: more health for the buck, as it were. The ultimate unit of outcome I know of captures in theory the intangible quality-of-life benefits we have been talking about. It is the quality-adjusted life year or QALY, advocated by Alan Williams. Remember, the quality-adjusted life year or QALY expresses a year of fully healthy life as 1. A year of life in a coma might have a relative value at about zero. Somewhere in between is the year of life of a rheumatoid arthritis sufferer – say 0.7. If alternative therapy at $10 raises this to 0.8 and auranofin at $15 raises it to 0.9, auranofin is more cost-effective because the alternative adds a tenth of a QALY at $10 each whereas auranofin adds a tenth of QALY at $7.50 each. Adding a whole QALY, collectively in a group of patients, might cost $1,000 for the alternative therapy but $750 for auranofin. That's the theory. However abstruse it seems we had to reckon with it when we planned to evaluate the socioeconomic benefits of auranofin.

Let me say as an aside that after spending a number of years in marketing research, and more recently in the middle of cost-benefit evaluations, when planning to go out and gather data and find out 'what is the answer', I hear more and more Gertrude Stein repeating over my shoulder her apt rejoinder, 'What is the question?' In most data endeavours, when all is said and done, the results will come down to a short phrase or a simple ratio on a blank piece of paper which summarizes the essence of what you've learned. This means at the beginning that if you don't state your hypothesis fully and clearly, you can spend months and millions riding off in all directions pursuing irrelevant or unconnected data. Well, our hypothesis was that we would find that: [QALY/$1 Auranofin] would be greater than [QALY/$1 Alternative]. And this determined what information we had to get, somehow, from a randomised double-blind clinical trial.

Outcome measures in a clinical trial

Having repeated to you the theory, perhaps to the limit of endurance, I want to turn now to the more practical aspects of our charge: to derive cost-benefit data from the context of a clinical trial.

For those of you who have never sat down and helped plan an RCT, a randomised clinical trial, it is a fascinating experience right at the centre of the business of developing and introducing new chemical entities. Traditionally the Phase III trials, those required for approval of a new chemical entity, are designed by company physicians and statisticians in cooperation with the pharmacologists, chemists and other physicians who have previously defined the drug's basic actions, toxicities, and doses in animals and limited human trials. There is a cardinal goal of the Phase III trial: regulatory approval. Of course, the drug's claims of benefit come largely from the Phase III results, so Marketing should and perhaps usually does have a say in what exactly these trials are designed to prove. Regulatory approval does not, and I hope never will, depend on proof of cost-benefit or cost-effectiveness. Also, regulatory authorities and their physician advisors are most comfortable with the 'harder' less-controversial measures of efficacy. In the case of arthritis these include: number of tender joints, number of swollen joints, grip strength in millimetres of mercury, time to walk fifty feet, time to onset of fatigue, duration of morning stiffness, patient-rated measure of pain or pain relief (often on a ten centimetre line), and global assessment of change in disease activity. Actually, the last is really quite subjective. There are also various chemical determinations such as ESR, haemoglobin, rheumatoid factor, technetium uptake, and xenon clearance, which may not correlate well with the other measures.

Auranofin had been tested against *injectable* gold by these traditional measures in clinical trials planned well before cost-benefit considerations were brought to bear. As I said, auranofin *also* had to be tested as an add-on oral therapy among appropriate patients taking typical anti-inflammatories or NSAIDS. In terms of RCT, this meant one group of patients were assigned at random a placebo and another group auranofin, with both groups allowed to continue their background of NSAIDS. Injectable gold and other remittive agents were excluded. For this trial, as a pure piggy-back on the traditional clinical and regulatory purposes, we designed a two-page series of economic questions to go into the case report form. The clinical investigators, the rheumatologists at different centres participating in the trial, were to ask these questions to their patients in the trial. Questions not only about workdays missed but about work changes, hired help at home, utilisation of medical services outside those mandated by the trial, and other economics-related items were put in this auranofin study. I struggled to create a single telling question that would capture in a nutshell as much of quality-of-life as possible. At the baseline or pretreatment point, it was: 'What is the most important thing to you that arthritis keeps you from doing?' Then at each subsequent visit the question was, in effect, 'How much of that activity have you been doing lately?' This question reflects the notion that in arthritis the goals and benefits of therapy in terms of functioning in life may be defined differently by each patient.

What we learned, or really confirmed, by this effort is: 1) that it is very difficult to construct questionnaires on utilisation of services – that is, cost-relevant events – in a precise enough way to analyse the results; 2) that it is impossible to do so in two pages; and 3) that even if you had the proper logical sequence of questions and many pages to ask them with, many physicians just cannot devote the time to learn the questioning techniques and administer the questionnaire during a medical visit. I now believe it is wrong methodologically to ask them to do so. As any good market-researcher or social-science interviewer knows, you have to be trained to ask survey questions verbatim, not lead, not intimidate, probe neutrally, and so on; not to mention follow the arrows and put the x's in the right boxes. Medical expertise and education do not necessarily qualify someone to do this. You need a certain type of person willing to be trained as a friendly neutral person and take pride, during the interview, in being so. An intelligent housewife can be better at it than you or I, or a physician or nurse. Medical knowledge can induce second-guessing and be an actual hinderance. I'll come back to interviewing later. Fourth and finally, the last thing we confirmed was that, if utilisation of services is hard to capture, quality of life is ten times more resistant to meaningful measurement. We really knew this; it was confirmed in spades. I doubt we shall ever make any quantifiable sense out of these two pages, which were an experimental rider onto a standard clinical trial.

It was then that we bit the bullet and conceived of a pre-marketing clinical trial much like the first one but specifically designed to answer our quality-of-life and cost-of-disease question. I will tell you how this conception was firmed up, adopted, and implemented.

We were lucky at the start, in a sense, because of the dissatisfaction among some eminent rheumatologists with the meaningfulness of the traditional measures of efficacy in arthritis treatment. If outcomes is the 'name of the game' in health care in these cost-conscious days, it is clearly so in rheumatology, where 'process' measures have substituted for more patient-oriented 'outcome' measures. As René Dubois has pointed out, 'The measurable drives out the important.' The question is, 'How do you know if a patient is better?' She may have fewer swollen joints but a more painful single joint. She may squeeze up the mercury higher in the grip strength test but walk the fifty feet slower. She may have less pain but get fatigued sooner. The most obvious indicator in routine cases is probably the physician's global rating of disease activity: none, mild, moderate, or severe. But this is not a 'hard' measurement as the others are. So some rheumatologists and students of outcome measurement were very interested in helping us find and adopt broader but objective measures of benefit. We met over several months to find the most reliable and best validated 'instruments' – as they are called – usable in a clinical trial situation. There was no perfect instrument. Some asked about activities of daily living; some emphasised small hand movements; others asked about mental states such as depression, self-image and attitudes towards health; others asked about utilisation of health care services and work lost – obviously important for our cost of disease evaluation; others asked in detail about the quality of pain experienced; and so on. Some were obviously arthritis-specific, others were not. Some were well validated; others were not. Some asked the patient what he was able to do – get out of the house, for example; others asked what the patient actually *did* do. With almost all of them, there was the question of scoring and weighting of scores. What if a patient at baseline could lift a jar down from a cupboard but not dress herself? Two months later she cannot lift the jar but can dress herself. Is she better or not? Perhaps, if dressing is more important to that patient, it should be mathematically-weighted more; then, the patient would be improved. Most of the instruments of this type essentially add the items to get a total score. There is another problem with such a score. If it is arthritis-specific, how meaningful is it to economists and policy makers who need to allocate funds among different therapeutic or preventive programmes? Suppose we find that a dollar of auranofin therapy produces a 15 per cent greater improvement in the Teeling Smith Arthritis Activities Inventory than does a dollar of control therapy. The winner in arthritis is clear enough. But what if one dollar spent on a non-sedating allergy medicine produces a 20 per cent improvement on the Paterson Index of Task Function? Where should the dollar be spent? We need a common unit of outcome, like the QALY that can be applied across different diseases.

Eclectic battery

An ideal instrument, then, would 1) be well validated 2) cover a broad range of life, not just buttoning vests or opening jars, to deserve the name quality of life, 3) ask about what patients actually did, not just what they said they were able to do, 4) weight the various items asked about according to patient or community evaluations of importance, so that the final score represents a preference-weighted outcome, and 5) produce a final score that has economic meaning across different diseases. Well, we found the closest thing we could to such an instrument, the Bush Health Status Index. Some call it a Rolls-Royce of health status evaluation. I would like to go into it briefly, since it illustrates how broad measures of health status tie in with cost and ultimately with policy decisions. I will quote and illustrate liberally from a recent paper by Atkins, Kaplan, *et al*, explaining the Health Status Index as used in a study![1] I quote:

> The Index places each individual into one of 43 mutually exclusive and collectively exhaustive levels of functioning. The levels of functioning are obtained from three separate scales of functioning: mobility (with five levels), physical activity (with four levels), and social activity (with five levels) . . . (See Table 1).
>
> The 43 levels of functioning are unique combinations of the steps of the scales shown . . . Although there are theoretically 100 possible combinations of these items, only 43 have been observed to date . . .
>
> In addition to these levels of function, each patient is classified according to the symptom or problem that bothered him/her the most. There are 36 such complexes of symptoms and problems . . . In previous research, each combination of Function Level and Symptom/ Problem Complex has been rated by random samples from the community to determine the weight or preference associated with the classification . . . The questionnaire has been validated in previous studies (Anderson and Bush) . . .

From the article, Table 2 shows a patient – M.R. – at study initiation. It is a pulmonary disease study. From a carefully constructed questionnaire administered to her by an interviewer it is determined that she was in the

TABLE 1   **Dimensions and steps for function levels in the quality of well-being scale**

Mobility	Physical activity	Social activity
Drove car and used bus or train without help (5)	Walked without physical problems (4)	Did work, school, or housework and other activities (5)
Did not drive, or had help to use bus or train (4)	Walked with physical limitations (3)	Did work, school, or housework but other activities limited (4)
In house (3)	Moved own wheelchair without help (2)	
In hospital (2)	In bed or chair (1)	Limited in amount or kind of work, school or housework (3)
In special care unit (1)		Performed self-care but not work, school or housework (2)
		Had help with self-care (1)

house, in bed or chair, had help with self-care activities and that the symptom or problem that bothered her the most was coughing, wheezing, or shortness of breath. Each of these descriptions has a scale step or level. I quote again:

> The weight the community associates with this level of functioning is 0.5129 with the adjustment of − 0.0075 for symptom/problem 11. So the preference weight for this case description is 0.5054. In other words an actual patient was classified into this level of function at time 1. In order to determine the social preference or weight for this condition, values obtained in a random-sample community survey were applied. In this case, the preference for the condition is 0.5054. This means that community members value this objective level of function about half way between optimum function (1.0) and death (0.0).

Table 3 shows M.R. at a later point in the study. Her social activity level has improved from a 1 to a 2. Everything else is the same. The preference weight associated with this state of functioning is 0.5715. The adjustment

TABLE 2   **'Before' index data**

Description	Level
In house	Mobility 3
In bed or chair	Physical Activity 1
Had help with self-care activities	Social Activity 1
Coughing, wheezing, or shortness of breath	Symptom/problem 11

Coughing, wheezing, or shortness of breath
$$\begin{array}{r} 0.5129 \\ -0.0075 \\ \hline 0.5054 \end{array}$$

Source   Adapted from C J Atkins, R M Kaplin, *et al*, Behavioral Programs for Exercise Compliance in Chronic Obstructive Pulmonary Disease; *J Consulting and Clin Psych.*

H

TABLE 3 'After' index data

Description	Level
In house	Mobility 3
In bed or chair	Physical Activity 1
Performed self-care but not work, school, or housework	Social Activity 2
Coughing, wheezing, or shortness of breath	Symptom/problem 11

$$0.5715$$
$$-0.0075$$
$$\overline{0.5640} \qquad 0.5640 - 0.5054 = 0.0586$$

Source Adapted from C J Atkins, R M Kaplin, *et al*, Behavioral Programs for Exercise Compliance in Chronic Obstructive Pulmonary Disease; *J Consulting and Clin Psych.*

for the symptom or problem is again − 0.0075, so the final weigth is 0.5640. I quote:

> The difference between the two states . . . is 0.0586 units of well-being [0.5640 minus the earlier 0.5054]. If this difference is maintained for one year, the production of well years is 0.0586 well years. If this bene-fit is accrued for 100 people, the benefit would be 5.86 well years . . . Another way to think of this benefit is that it is a perceived 5.86 per cent improvement in the quality of life.

There are obviously a number of complex techniques and assumptions involved in this model. I have trouble keeping them all in mind and refer you to articles by Bush and Kaplan and by their commentators. I think you can see that the Index, in theory at least, promises to fulfil our need for cost-effectiveness ratios with a common, broad unit of outcome. Hopefully, dividing the net cost of non-steroidal anti-inflammatories (NSAIDS) plus auranofin-treated patients by their well years produced will provide a more favourable ratio than the cost of the NSAIDS-plus placebo-treated patients divided by their well years produced. The Bush-Kaplan model also provides a common measure for the comparison of programmes with different specific objectives. For example, hypertension screening programmes pro-duced a well year at about $10,000 each. Hospital renal dialysis costs more than $50,000 to produce a well year. So we also hope to see how these com-pare with rheumatoid arthritis treatment with auranofin.

Life is not easy, however. Remember, the Index is for all diseases, not just rheumatoid arthritis. The measured improvements in level may be, in a sense, major functional steps. So, would the Index be sensitive enough to detect the differences between the two groups in our randomised clinical trial? For that matter, would any of the non-traditional instruments, even the arthritis specific ones, be sensitive enough? Most or all had not been used in controlled drug trials. Our decision was eclectic: use the Bush Index, but also use other instruments, one quite arthritis specific, one focusing more on mental state, one on utilisation of services, and so on. Our consul-tants carefully selected the best battery of instruments, and we obtained permission from their originators for use in our clinical trial.

Let me indicate one or two questions from each of the outcome instru-ments, so you will get a feel for what they sound like:

- Over the past week, were you able to turn faucets on and off? Without any difficulty – with some difficulty – with much difficulty – or unable to do?
- Were you able to climb up five steps?
- My health is a concern in my life: Definitely true, mostly true, don't know, mostly false, definitely false?
- With reference to your rheumatoid arthritis, how do you assess your condition today? Would you say it is: very poor, poor, fair, good, very good?
- Since [the start of the study] would you say your ability to use transport has changed to become: a lot better, somewhat better, somewhat worse, a lot worse, or has there been no change at all?
- How long do you do light work before you must take at least a few minutes break?
- I am going to show you a card with groups of words that describe pain. Some of the groups contain words that describe *your present pain*. Please tell me the single word in each group that applies best:
  tugging, pulling, wrenching
  annoying, troublesome, miserable, intense, unbearable.
- On which of the past 6 days, if any, did you drive a car? What was the reason that you did not drive on (day X)? (If no driver's licence) What is the reason you do not now have a driver's licence?
  In addition to (that/reason), were there any other reasons related in any way to your health that you did not drive on (that day)?
  Do you ever use public transportation . . . (etc)?
- [In the past four weeks,] have you seen a rheumatologist, surgeon (etc)?
  Did you have to take time off from work? How much time off did you take?
  Did you have to pay someone to babysit?
  Did you have other expenses . . . ?
  How many miles did you travel?
- How many days out of the last 7 days would you say:
  You felt fearful?
  People were unfriendly?
  You felt sad?

This is just a random sampling. It gives an idea of the method.

In addition it was decided to repeat most of the traditional measures used in arthritis drug trials: joint counts, grip strength, etc. It was important to compare and, in a way, validate results in the new, broader outcome measures against results with the traditional measures. These measures, of course, are made by the clinical investigators, not lay interviewers.

So far, then, we had these ingredients of a study: 1) the context of a double-blind randomised trial 2) traditional measures of outcome made by physicians and 3) a battery of new measures of outcome and cost obtained from questionnaires given by interviewers. Then we had to settle on how many patients would be needed for statistical significance. This took much discussion because broader benefit measures were often lacking or could not be applied to the comparative trial situation. By comparison, variance calculations with the traditional measures were relatively old hat. In sum, a large number of patients was judged necessary.

Interview constraints

I come back now to one of the most interesting constraints on this trial, the patient interviews. How could we work them in? The patients were scheduled for medical evaluation and traditional assessment by the physician at minus 2 weeks and o-day baseline and then once a month for the six month period. That's a total of 8 visits. Not all of the newer outcome instruments, some rather lengthy, could be administered each time. Various ones could be staggered, however. Nonetheless, we predicted from pre-tests that over all eight visits they would take around 16 hours of a patient's time. For the patient that comes to an average of two hours of interview time, plus traditional clinical time, at each visit. For the interviewer, preparation of forms before the interview and filling out of forms after the interview would add another two hours per interview. All this was obviously too demanding on both time and interviewer costs. In more pre-tests the battery of instruments was pruned to 8 hours and 18 minutes per patient predicted over the six month period, or 62 minutes per average interview. The interviews have in fact averaged 58 minutes each, with the interviewer spending about another hour in pre-and post-interview clerical time. One effect of this on the investigator was the need to schedule their trial patients' visits far enough apart during the week or on visit days for the interviewer to have time to administer the questionnaires. The major implication of the personal interview system, however, was the need to have a resident interviewer at each investigational centre. This meant a limited number of centres, because we could not station interviewers all across the country. Thus, the centre had to be large enough or active enough to recruit a minimum of 20 patients. Twenty patients would keep an interviewer busy perhaps half time, but not at predictable hours. Thus, interviewers had to be recruited among people willing to work odd hours on a part-time basis. It was obvious, too, that once in the trial the patient was scheduled for monthly medical examinations which could not be delayed. The outcome interviews had to be given in synch and also could not be delayed. What would happen if the interviewer took sick, had to move, tired of the job or for other reasons had to quit? We could not risk this and decided on back-up interviewers at almost all centres, with each back-up doing a certain minimum of the interviewing in order to keep up proficiency. I think you can sense the logistical complexity of patient scheduling and of interview scheduling at the centre and all the paper work involved with medical and outcome forms and questionnaires. It became clear that a study coordinator was also required at each centre. The team at each centre thus became the rheumatologist investigator, the study co-ordinator, the quality-of-life interviewer, and the back-up interviewer. I should add that clinical drug trials traditionally require that representatives from the company's drug-development area visit the physician investigators regularly to assure completeness of medical data recording, adherence to the trial protocol, and so on. These people were also routinely involved from time to time at each centre.

Who were the quality-of-life interviewers and how were they directed? First off, we knew that an outside organisation had to be found to train the interviewers, monitor and control the quality of their performance in the field, and receive, process and code their data. We also wanted an organisation with computerisation facilities and expertise, and the expertise needed to perform analyses of the quality of the data from a survey research point of view. We found such an organisation. Together we decided that if it was to be responsible for the interviewers' performance and the quality of the data, the interviewers must report to the organisation[2] and be exclusively in their employ. This meant the interviewer could not be a member of the investigator's staff. The study coordinator, however, had to be. The centres then found and proposed candidates for the interviewer position. SK&F met with the candidates at each site, and the best were hired by the outside health-care research organisation. The interviewers were sent home-study materials and then brought together for an intense training session lasting about a week. Of course, preceding the training was the constant pre-testing of the questionnaires and the preparation of training interviews, tapes, instruction manuals, and other materials. The interviewers went back to their cities of residence and began interviewing. However, at some centres the start of the trial was delayed. Institutional review boards, proper patient consent forms, last minute modifications in medical exclusion criteria, and such things can often delay a centre's start date. So the interviewers had to do practice interviews to keep up their skills. Also, since not all centres could be recruited at once, additional training sessions were required for interviewers hired later at these centres. All interviewers were required to tape-record the first five interviews for close review by the outside organisation. Errors in interview technique and data recording were scrupulously and relentlessly pointed out and eliminated. Constant critiques and supervision by the outside organisation were maintained. I have never seen such intense, hands-on, quality-control in a research survey. I dare say it rarely occurs. But, with instruments that some would call 'soft' in themselves, we had at all costs to avoid any possibility of softness in the data collection.

Have I discouraged you? Let me add that the trial would generate two streams of paper work. By one stream, the quality-of-life data, recorded in triplicate, were sent directly to the outside organisation – with a copy to SK&F. We had to monitor it all for AOTES (adverse on-therapy experiences) reported by the patient to the interviewer, even if scribbled in the margin. The second stream of data was the traditional medical-examination data recorded by the investigators on traditional case report forms and relayed to SK&FS Medical Affairs Department. These forms are immediately reviewed for AOTES and then processed and coded for traditional analysis of efficacy. The two streams thus pile up on computers at separate organisations. Experts at SK&F and the outside organisation are planning the merger, at SK&F, of the two files. The quality-of-life file alone contains data from over 2,400 hours of patient interviewing.

On the upbeat side, let me say that the interviewers have stayed with us and done a superb job. Personal commitment to the study goals and tasks has been a vital ingredient here. The interview data is remarkably complete – probably 95 per cent to 99 per cent overall. Inter-observer reliability checks show similarly high percentages. For each questionnaire, we know where interviewers have most difficulty, where patients may misinterpret most easily, and what extraneous comments are made. As an aside, I wonder whether traditional 'hard' medical data, recorded on case report forms by physicians in traditional clinical trials, can be obtained with any-where near this degree of standardisation. In any case, the interview system has worked as planned, although you can imagine the details of planning, communication, and execution that were involved. The more traditional side – recruitment of centres, institutional review, and patient enrolment – has also worked. Most important, very few patients have dropped out of the trial. This problem, bugaboo in many a trial, appears minimal. In short, the process seems well so far. I am pleased by the rigour of both the trial design and the data-collection process, and I am excited by the richness of the data we shall have.

Outcomes in the community

I close with a question: Will the findings about auranofin in the ideal condi-tions of a randomised trial hold true in the real world of the community? In the real world different kinds of patients will take the drug, some will not comply with the dosage, most will not receive as much medical attention as in a clinical trial, and few if any will take placebos as an alternative. Thus, it seems important, as we did with 'Tagamet', to observe a natural population over time. Special quality-of-life measures and cost-of-disease measures would have to be applied to auranofin and non-auranofin patients, since no ongoing survey collects these data. Since no randomisation is present, patient selection bias would occur and have to be controlled for. Can such a study be done? My answer is 'yes'. We are doing that study, too! The 'before' phase is in progress now, in the United States. But that in itself is a whole other subject. Having come back to it for the sake of conceptual completeness, I must leave details until another time.

REFERENCES

1   C J Atkins, R M Kaplan, *et al*, Behavioral Program for Exercise Compliance in Chronic Obstructive Pulmonary Disease, *J Consulting and Clin Psych*, in press, by permission of the authors.
2   Rhode Island Health Services Research Inc., Providence, R.I.

Economics of bone marrow transplantation

Humphrey Kay
Royal Marsden Hospital, London

Bone marrow transplantation (BMT) is an effective therapeutic procedure in cases of aplastic anaemia, acute leukaemias, chronic myeloid leukaemia, certain immunodeficiency states and some metabolic disorders. It may also be found to be useful in some other neoplastic disorders, immune dysfunctions and, last but not least, in thalassaemia and haemoglobinopathies.

As an illustration of its efficacy at low cost I should like to quote the first case we treated on the Seattle protocol in 1973.[1] This was a boy of seven with bone marrow aplasia following hepatitis – a condition with a mortality of almost 100 per cent. He was lucky enough to have a major-histo-compatible-antigen-identical donor, his only sister, and the transplant was done without problems or complications, He was nursed in isolation for five weeks and this was a a matter of concern to some of the nurses. (Isolation in this context means bacteriological isolation: the availability of television, telephone, an outside window, unlimited visitors the other side of a plastic panel and a generous quota of nurses implies a minimum degree of psychological isolation.) At the end of the time the mother was interviewed regarding the psychological effect on her son. Yes, it had affected him she said 'it has brought him on so; he's so articulate'. Now, ten years later, he leads a normal life and when he recently undertook a sponsored walk for charity it wasn't in aid of marrow transplantation as he was under the impression that all the problems had been solved.

Such a case illustrates the best that bone marrow transplantation can offer and it is important to emphasise the restrictions. First of all, with exceptions which I shall mention, it is still largely confined to those with a histocompatible donor, – in practice a brother or sister who has, on a one in four genetic chance, inherited the same HLA genes from their parents. Secondly there is an age restriction; very few transplants are successful after the age of forty and there is an increasing incidence from childhood through early adult life of one of the main complications, graft-versus-host disease (GVHD). Success is also prejudiced by the presence of infection, of preceding blood transfusions, and preceding cytotoxic drug therapy, so that in any analysis of the relative costs and benefits the area of maximum success and greatest benefit will be surrounded by a very wide penumbra of less successful, complication-ridden cases, with no clearly demarcated boundaries. Furthermore, as techniques evolve and are improved and also, as follow-up reveals the existence and frequency of long-term complications, the whole equation of cost and benefit can change profoundly.

In 1979 we undertook a rather approximate cost-benefit analysis for one main group of patients, namely young patients with acute myeloid leukaemia in first remission with a matched donor.[2] The basis of this analysis was to take the standard cost of both in-patients and out-patients at the Royal

111

Marsden Hospital, Sutton, and to estimate for each item, eg nursing care, radiology, pharmacy, by how much a transplant patient cost more or less than the other hospital patients and then to aggregate the costs for a period until death, relapse or – as was the case for the majority – for one year of leukaemia-free survival from the date of transplant.

The main deficiencies of such an analysis – apart from its intrinsic inaccuracies – are firstly that it takes no account of capital costs; secondly the procedures used certain drugs for which no charge was made, in particular cyclosporin-A and acyclovir, and thirdly the period of one year for follow-up is arbitrary and short. Admittedly the costs and the chances of relapse or other complications are very much smaller after one year but occasional late relapses, late infections, chronic GVHD, second neoplasms and other complications such as cataracts must be expected in a proportion of patients and these will all adversely affect the sum of benefit.

The capital cost is an important item but it is not one that is taken into account in the standard NHS cost estimates. To do marrow transplants in the best way some degree of protective isolation and some special facilities such as apparatus for whole body irradiation, blood separators, etc, are required. Our unit at the Marsden Hospital was built entirely with charity-raised money and cost £100,000 just over 10 years ago – and a recently-installed unit for whole-body irradiation has cost just under £400,000 – also funded by charities and grant-giving bodies. The current rent or amortisa-

TABLE 1   **Costs of BMT in 1978–79 and 1981–82**

	1978–79 per day	1981–82 per day
Nursing	£30.00	£67.00
Medical	£6.50	£10.70
Pharmacy	£7.28	£12.46
Medical supplies	£8.15	£15.00
Radiology	£1.13	£2.44
Pathology	£7.10	£11.80
General hospital services	£35.43	£46.00
	£95.60	£165.40
In-patient costs: for 43.6 days	£4,168	for 43.8 days £7,244
Radiotherapy	£245	£370
Tissue-typing	£650	£1,000
Blood-bank	£250	£300
Donor costs	£250	£400
Out-patients	£500	£722
Cost in one year	£6,013	£10,036
		(Acyclovir £397)
		(Cyclosporin-A £2,437)
		£12,870

TABLE 2 **Case-material for analysis**

All BMT for AML at Royal Marsden Hospital
May 1981 – April 1982. Follow-up to 30 April 1983

Matched transplants:		
In first remission		15
In second or later remission		6

Mismatched transplants:		
In first remission		5
In second or later remission		10
Total		36

Age		
< 20	12	
20–29	7	Mean age 26.1
30–39	14	
$\geqslant 40$	3	

tion of these facilities would not be less than £100,000 per annum or about £2,000 per transplant.

Table 1 presents the figures as published in the *Lancet* for 1978–79 and those for 1981–82. The biggest difference is for nursing – the same number, but more highly paid nurses – and the smallest is for general hospital services – among the post-graduate hospitals the Royal Marsden Hospital spends a uniquely low fraction of its budget on administration. The original estimates contained no sums for cyclosporin-A and acyclovir, two drugs which were and are extensively used. In 1978–79 and 1981–82 they were on trial without cost but from 1983 they will be charged so I have included a sum which is based on the actual usage in 1981–82 and the proposed cost in 1983. The other costs are roughly as one might expect but paradoxically the cost of tissue-typing has not gone up as much as one would expect. This is because in 1978–79 we only undertook fully-matched transplants and therefore had to type four families to find one with a matched patient and donor, while in 1981–82 many of the transplants were done as mismatched haplotype identical transplants so that less of the typing information was wasted. These figures, however, refer only to first remission matched transplants so as to be comparable with those published in 1980.

If we analyse the total transplants from May 1981 to April 1982 (Table 2) we can see there are four categories of patients with acute myeloid leukaemia (AML). Those with mismatched transplants are essentially an experimental group, mostly in second remission and therefore, with a hopeless prognosis. However these four categories do illustrate the law of diminishing returns as one proceeds from the best prognosis cases to those least likely to be salvaged – nevertheless they include a few outstanding successes in patients otherwise doomed. This is how the potential of bone marrow transplantation was first established and how it will probably progress.

The relative costs based on in-patient and out-patient care and on the cost of cyclosporin-A and acyclovir as it would be now are shown in Table 3 to Table 6.

TABLE 3   **First remission AML 1981–82. Matched donors**

15 patients, ages 12–44 (mean 26.3)
As in-patient 28–84 days (mean 43.8)
As out-patient 0–31 attendances (mean 17.2)
Acyclovir cost 0–£2,000 (mean £397)
Cyclosporin-A cost £360–£5,160 (mean £2,437)
Costs in first year £8,785–£21,040 (mean £12,870)
Disease-free survivors at 30/4/83   8/15

TABLE 4   **Second or later remission AML 1981–82. Matched donors**

6 patients, ages 6–39 (mean 25.5)
As in-patient 28–67 days (mean 43.1)
As out-patient 0–29 attendances (mean 20.3)
Acyclovir cost 0–£1,300 (mean £303)
Cyclosporin-A cost £400–£9,650 (mean £4,000)
Costs in first year £9,815–£18,855 (mean £14,160)
Disease-free survivors at 30/4/83   3/6

TABLE 5   **First remission AML 1981–82. Mismatched donors**

5 patients, ages 15–44 (mean 26.6)
As in-patient 25–71 days (mean 57.4)
As out-patient 0–32 attendances (mean 14)
Acyclovir cost 0–£1,150 (mean £600)
Cyclosporin-A cost £340–£6,600 (mean £3,900)
Costs in first year £6,610–£21,885 (mean £15,650)
Disease-free survivors at 30/4/83   2/5

TABLE 6   **Second or later remission AML 1981–82. Mismatched donors**

10 patients, ages 3–44 (mean 23.1)
As in-patient 23–102 days (mean 59.8)
As out-patient 0–24 attendances (mean 8.4)
Acyclovir cost 0–£11,320 (mean £1,670)
Cyclosporin-A cost £300–£4,000 (mean £1,470)
Costs in first year £6,465–£26,630 (mean £15,515)
Disease-free survivors at 30/4/83   2/10

These patients have been followed-up for 1 to 2 years, thus including the period of greatest mortality and risk of relapse – although a few further losses in all groups may occur – and from the survivors at the end of last month one can then estimate the cost per survivor in each group (Table 7). If we then optimistically assume that these survivors may complete a normal life span, ie to the age of 65, we can derive the cost for each year of life gained. Of course, that figure is the best possible and there will be penalties of an unpredictable degree to come. There have been one or two relapses in all series in the second and third years, second neoplasms have been reported and late infections are also a risk. We had a death due to pneumococcal infection and another fatal fungal infection at 18 months and two years from transplant respectively. However even if the costs were doubled by these losses, the amounts paid per year of life are mostly well within the

TABLE 7 **Relative costs and potential survival of AML BMT patients**

	First remission match	Later remission match	First remission mismatch	Later remission mismatch
Mean cost per patient	£12,870	£14,160	£15,650	£15,515
Cost per survivor at 30/4/83	£24,037	£28,320	£39,125	£77,575
Potential survival to 65 years	304 years	90 years	89 years	118 years
Cost per year of life gained	£633	£944	£879	£1,319

margins of what these young adults are mostly earning and spending on drink, tobacco, holidays or education.

I should mention two other points. Is bone marrow transplantation the best treatment for AML? One series of cases, treated at Boston by intensive chemotherapy only,[3] suggests that results which are very nearly as good can be obtained, especially in children. However, it is intensive therapy; the time spent in hospital – on average 80 days – and the amount of supportive treatment required results in a cost and in a stress imposed on the patient which are not very different from that of a marrow transplant.

Secondly, marrow transplantation is, of course, still in the phase of development where all sorts of exciting new procedures and devices are being tried but where the long-term prospects are largely unpredictable. In ten or twenty years time a more accurate assessment of its costs and benefits may be possible.

REFERENCES

1 Royal Marsden Hospital Bone Marrow Transplant Team. 'Bone Marrow Aplasia after Infectious Hepatitis Treated by Bone Marrow Transplantation'. *British Medical Journal*, 1974; 1: 363–364.

2 Kay H E M, Powles R L, Lawler S D, Clink H M, 'Cost of Bone Marrow Transplants in Acute Myeloid Leukaemia'. *Lancet* 1980; 1067–1069.

3 Weinstein H J, Mayer R J, Rosenthal D S, Camitta B M, Coral F S, Nathan D G, Frei E III. 'Treatment of Acute Myelogenous Leukemia in Children and Adults'. *New England Journal of Medicine*, 1980; 9: 473–478.

ACKNOWLEDGEMENTS

1 The data are presented on behalf of the Leukaemia Unit; the work was supported through a number of sources but we are particularly grateful to the Leukaemia Research Fund and the Bud Flanagan Leukaemia Fund.

Measurement of the benefits in respiratory disease

Dr Duncan Geddes
Brompton & London Chest Hospital

Respiratory disease is very widespread, ranging from the common cold to the commonest cancer in man. I thought that it would be most helpful to look at chronic respiratory disability for three reasons. First because it fits in quite well with some other subjects in this volume. Secondly, it is a very prevalent condition in the community with about half a million people in England and Wales suffering severe or partial disability from chronic lung disease. Thirdly, chronic lung disease provides a rare opportunity actually to measure the disease itself and its components in terms of a symptom and in terms of a social consequence.

So let us start with a simple model.

Lung disease ⟶ Breathlessness ⟶ Immobility

We have a lung disease which produces a very familiar sensation or symptom, namely breathlessness which results in a disadvantage in terms of immobility with social consequences attached to it. So if our treatment is to be effective, we obviously hope to make the lung disease better, reduce the symptom and improve the mobility. The conventional way of looking at this has been to ignore the symptom and to go from lung disease to immobility in the expectation that by improving lung function the patient will get better and his mobility be improved. What I want to do is to explore the relationship between the disease, the symptom and the consequence. It is convenient because we can measure all three with some reasonable precision.

Lung function can be measured in a lung function laboratory, where ventilatory volumes and gas transfer are assessed. Questionnaires and the symptom of breathlessness we will talk about separately. I am going to take exercise tolerance as the gold standard because in the end that is what we want to improve. We want to improve an individual's mobility so that he can get out of his house, go shopping, manage to go to the pub, and live a normal life. The conventional way of measuring exercise tolerance has been to use the methods of the exercise physiology laboratory and exercise patients on a cycle ergometer so that they pedal against an increasing resistance . This method is suitable for assessing athletes or normal subjects but it is really of limited value in assessing respiratory cripples because they often stop too soon and the form of exercise used has little reference to their day-to-day life. Similarly, treadmills have been tried but if the patient is old or somewhat unsteady, he may find this form of exercise very difficult, so a treadmill test is not very suitable either.

Perhaps the best common sense advance that has happened during the last decade in respiratory medicine is the corridor walk. The patient is asked to cover as much ground as he can walking in twelve minutes up and down a corridor. He can stop and rest if required. In that way we get a measure of how much he can do while performing normal exercise. The distance walked turns out to be quite surprisingly reproducible, as reproducible as any of the lung function tests, and slightly better than most. After a few practices, individual patients walk at a remarkably constant speed with a variability of about 5 per cent.

So we have a reasonably good measure of exercise tolerance which is reproducible, which is not very distressing to the patient, which is cheap, and which is somewhat like everyday life. Furthermore, an individual patient walks at a constant speed, so it does not really matter whether we look at a twelve-minute distance or a six-minute distance. That is what I am going to use nearly all the way through this paper as the gold standard.

So the first question to ask is: How well does lung function correlate with corridor walk? In other words, do lung function tests give you a proper measure of disability? They do not. The correlation of walking distance with Forced Expiratory Volume (FEV) is poor. The correlation with vital capacity which effectively measures how much lung is available to breathe with is a little better, and combination of the lung volume with its ability to exchange gas is better again. So there is a weak correlation between lung function, the disease that is being measured, and the final measured disadvantage.

I have taken examples from a few studies out of literature to illustrate the measured benefit of treatment. The percentage improvement in a measure of lung function (vital capacity) can be compared with our mobility, the twelve-minute walking distance. In this particular study the improvement in lung function with steroids was well-matched by the improvement in mobility. Similarly, examining the effect of salbutamol, we can see an improvement of about 10 per cent in lung function resulting in a similar improvement in mobility. In the same study in the same patients, a second drug was also given and this produced a considerably greater improvement in lung function with no further improvement in mobility. So there is a discrepancy between one measure, namely lung function which we thought we were interested in and another measure which is what the patient is interested in. So the conclusion so far is that lung function tells us something about mobility but it does not correlate well and does not necessarily give us the relevant measurement if we are going to make our patients walk down the street further. In fact, if we assess a treatment in terms of lung function and look at that only, we are going to put a number of patients on toxic and expensive treatment unnecessarily. We clearly have to think it through a little further.

Now let us consider breathlessness and see how well that correlates. We can measure breathlessness using the simple Medical Research Council (MRC) questionnaire. The details are not very important – in essence the questions range from normal to examples of how disabled the individual is by breathlessness. This works really quite well, but has two disadvantages. One is that very general questions are asked. The patient assesses his breathlessness during the past week in terms of distances and hills; but if he has not tried to walk a mile in the past week or if he has not been climbing hills, he is forced to integrate his experience over a much longer period. Secondly, there are only five grades and most patients fall into the top three, so the results are necessarily imprecise.

The next scale is the oxygen cost diagram, which is partly a visual analogue and partly a verbal analogue scale in which various everyday tasks are listed so that the patient can get some sort of targeting on what he can do before he marks the line. This has to my mind a number of disadvantages. It is rather a cumbersome scale to use; patients tend to concentrate on activities which are familiar rather than those which make them breathless, and different patients have very different habits. For example, some people are very energetic bedmakers, and some just throw the sheets back on so that breathlessness during bedmaking can mean different things. In practice the oxygen cost diagram does not work quite so well as the MRC questionnaire, although it provides greater precision.

So let us look at what the psychologists tell us is the purer way of doing it, a straightforward visual analogue scale which the patient marks between not breathless and extremely breathless. This has quite a big advantage. The question can refer to the last year, the last month, the last week, the last day, or even now, and patients can score their symptom while they are walking. So we are beginning to get near to what we want to measure. Most patients can use the scale easily and score in a reproducible way.

Let us look at the oxygen cost diagram and a simple visual analogue scale, and see how well they correlate with corridor walking distance. They correlate quite well and better than lung function tests.

Now let us look at these questionnaires in terms of response to treatment. We did a study which seemed to us sensible at the time. We asked a number of patients to come to the hospital early in the morning and gave them a drink of bitter lemon, containing either dihydrocodeine, or double vodka or caffeine equivalent to two cups of coffee. We were interested to know whether we would make any difference to their lung function, which we did not, and whether we would make any difference to their breathlessness, which we did. A change of breathlessness on visual analogue scale as compared to placebo (bitter lemon alone) occurred with dihydrocodeine. That was quite interesting. So here is a treatment which is affecting the symptom without affecting the cause of the symptom. The dihydrocodeine patients also walked further. Interestingly, the alcohol also improved walking distance. Patients have often said that they have to stop on the way to the pub two or three times but that they can walk all the way back. Quite what mechanism is involved, I am not sure.

Now let us consider oxygen; many patients claim benefit from breathing oxygen, which is often put down to placebo effect but measurements have seldom been made. Here oxygen is compared with air and this patient goes substantially further and records less breathlessness. So all systems seem to be working well. Why then bother with an analogue scale when walking distance demonstrates the benefit?

But here is another example. This patient does not walk any further with oxygen but while he is walking he is less breathless. So it is possible to improve the symptom without affecting exercise tolerance and this is a potential benefit of treatment which is very seldom either considered or measured.

Unfortunately, there are further difficulties with our simple model of lung disease $\longrightarrow$ breathlessness $\longrightarrow$ immobility. This chain of events continues for some time and the patient tends to sit at home immobile and not go out. He does not go out because he is breathless, and so he becomes unfit. As a result of that, he is more breathless for the same amount of exercise and so enters a vicious cycle. Furthermore, by sitting immobile at home he may become depressed, and depression tends to aggravate physical symptoms, so he gets worse for another reason. The original model is, therefore naive, and we have to think of these vicious cycles and consider trying to exploit them in treatment.

We have measured depression in a number of our patients and compared the result with their walking distance. Now we come up with the best correlation co-efficients that we have seen so far. In fact, while we originally thought that immobility was a simple consequence of lung disease, it is now clear that this was only a part of the story and the psychological reaction to the disability and symptom seems to be taking over as the major problem.

If you compare all of our different measurements with walking distance, lung function correlates only quite well; visual analogue scales better; depression best. This brings home the point that in trying to assess the individual patient we are likely to miss a lot of the picture if we just stay on physical symptoms alone. But how do you exploit this in terms of treatment?

In South Wales a study recently reported investigating the effect of an exercise programme on walking distance in patients with chronic lung disease. The treatment group came to the gym, swam in the swimming pools, and took part in a strenuous exercise programme. The control group came to the centre but did not take part in the programme until some weeks after the start of the study. What they found was that the treatment group definitely improved during the time that they were having active treatment and that improvement was sustained after the exercises were stopped. Surprisingly, the control group improved impressively as well, before their period of exercise. What I think is going on here is that they are treating both the depression and the lack of fitness together. Perhaps the control group had their depression treated by attending a centre and becoming involved in the study while the active treatment group improved faster because they were also becoming fitter. There is the caveat for anybody trying to do studies of this sort because the very fact that you have a patient in the study can make them better. But the good news was that they were able to sustain an effect.

So to summarise, we have measured lung function which was not very satisfactory, we have measured breathlessness which was better, and all the time we have been using a corridor walking distance as a gold standard. And, of course, it is not. The walking distance tells us nothing about what the patient is doing at home and whether there has been any change in his quality of life. How can we assess whether a treatment which can improve his potential mobility, has improved his actual mobility?

Visual analogue scales can be done at home every night and then we can compare a week on treatment with a week off treatment. In a trial using regular dihydrocodeine there was a significant improvement in daily visual analogue symptom scoring, so the treatment seems to work. There is, however, a further problem since one way of being less breathless is to lie in bed all day. So it is not necessarily true that if we improve the specific symptom we have done what we set out to do.

We tried to get round this, by asking patients to wear pedometers so that we could assess what they actually did during the day, at the same time as measuring how breathless they were doing it. The results were encouraging and it may be that simple measures like this, if used in association with the rather more complex measures we have discussed give the best assessment of all.

I would like to stop there, but there is one disturbing footnote. We have assumed all the time that what we want to do is to get patients to walk further. What we are after is to improve their mobility and there are, of course better ways of doing it. When a patient uses a bicycle instead of walking, he expends considerably less energy, goes very much further, and enjoys himself much more. These are aspects of his life we have not begun to consider measuring. It does just make us wonder whether the same amount of money and energy invested in some form of alternative transport rather than in doctors and drugs might not be worth considering in the balance of treating what is a disabling chronic disease.

Social criteria of the outcome of mental disease

Michael Shepherd

Institute of Psychiatry, London

Just over 100 years ago Henry Maudsley pointed out that 'it seems proper to emphasise the fact that insanity is really a social phenomenon, and to insist that it cannot be investigated satisfactorily and apprehended rightly except it be studied from a social point of view'.[1] The same opinion has since been voiced by a long line of authoritative figures and is now embodied in what has come to be called 'social psychiatry'.[2] At the scientific core of this hybrid sub-discipline is clinical epidemiology, which includes within its orbit the evaluation of remedies. In this paper I propose to discuss the background and development of this approach to mental disorder and some of the lessons to be derived from it, paying particular regard to the example of schizophrenia.

As a convenient point of departure we might go back 50 years to the mid-1930s, when Manfred Sakel introduced deep insulin coma as 'the first effective drug treatment of schizophrenia', claiming a 70 per cent full remission rate and a high proportion of what he termed, but did not define, 'social remission' in the remainder. For nearly 20 years a stream of studies purported to confirm this contention, most of them conducted by a small group of enthusiasts who paid little attention to the undercurrent of disbelief exhibited by a growing number of clinicians.

In 1953, however, these doubts received public expression in a paper published in the *Lancet* which challenged the theoretical basis and clinical efficacy of the treatment.[3] This article provoked a storm of largely intemperate criticism by the insulin-advocates to which the author responded in kind. The stage seemed set for further vigorous confrontations, when the dispute was overtaken by the appearance of the early reports of the treatment of schizophrenia by chlorpromazine. Within a surprisingly short period the situation had been transformed. Insulin-units had virtually disappeared after five years and the painstaking demonstration in 1959 that insulin-coma carried no advantage over barbiturate-induced sleep came too late. The issue was dead and, meanwhile, the pro-insulin faction had undergone a metamorphosis to become votaries at the shrine of psychopharmacology. None the less, during those few months in 1953 it became evident that more than an impersonal issue was being debated. What was at stake – as the title of the *Lancet* paper made clear – was essentially an article of belief, a myth, in this case 'The Insulin Myth'. In retrospect, I would like to suggest that the mythopoeic elements in question reflect what has been called the Oedipus Effect, a term which bears no relation to that better-known piece of psychiatric jargon, the Oedipus Complex. The notion of the Oedipus Effect was introduced by the philosopher and historian of science, Sir Karl Popper, whose reference to the unfortunate King of Thebes was radically different from Freud's and characteristically more accurate. By it

J

he referred to the influence of a prediction upon the event predicted, for in the story the oracle plays a key role in the sequence of events leading to the fulfilment of its own prophecy.

The two lessons of insulin-coma treatment which impressed themselves on me at the time, however, were practical rather than mythological. One of them was an interest in that ambiguous terms, 'social outcome', which had been used so loosely to describe the results of treatment, and I undertook a 5-year follow-up of all 126 schizophrenic patients who had received deep-insulin coma therapy at the Maudsley Hospital over a 3-year period.[4] The findings were instructive. In general, a good clinical outcome was associated with social independence and a history of having spent least time in hospital; conversely, a poor clinical outcome was linked with social dependency and a long hospital stay. However, the agreement between these three indices was far from complete and it was possible to demonstrate the need to separate and evaluate individual forms of clinical phenomena and social behaviour in assessing outcome.

The second lesson was the need for properly conducted studies of therapeutic evaluation in the field of mental illness. The opportunity was to arise shortly afterwards, when the Medical Research Council of Great Britain set up a committee for this very purpose. For some years the committee did not concern itself directly with the treatment of schizophrenia. The early batch of drugs introduced to treat schizophrenia were used to alleviate psychomotor excitement, later to provide a symptomatic treatment for the acute or chronic form of the condition. For various reasons it was felt that neither of these claims called for independent assessment but then, in the late 1960s, came a stream of oracular pronouncements on their value in the 'maintenance' or long-term treatment of patients whose state had already been improved by medication or who were symptom-free. The chorus became louder, and more insistent, with the arrival of long-acting injections which, it was claimed, coped with the problem of non-compliance posed by patients who failed to take oral medication. The speed with which 'maintenance' or – as it is more accurately termed – 'continuation' treatment became part of routine psychiatric practice was in itself a striking phenomenon, one which came to be called in some quarters the 'third revolution' in psychiatry (the first and second being psychoanalysis and the discovery of chlorpromazine respectively).

It may be remarked that the putative advantages attaching to continuation therapy were dominantly social in that they were said:
1) to facilitate the return of patients to the community,
2) to reduce the burden on the family, and
3) to render rehabilitation easier and more economical.
All these claims fitted well with the expectations of the day, and though the hard evidence delineating the efficacy of short- or long-acting neuroleptic continuation treatment was negligible, in Britain, as elsewhere, clinical opinion came to accept the view that a diagnosis of schizophrenia in hospital should lead to pharmacotherapy by the parenteral route in virtually every case. The Oedipus Effect was manifest once again.

Now when a major shift of opinion leads to a massive change, or lurch, in clinical practice the opportunity arises to monitor the situation by analysing the impact of such measures on the target-population. Since it is hardly possible to anticipate such situations, most cohort-studies have perforce to be carried out retrospectively, and for psychiatric illness a trend-analysis of this type becomes theoretically possible because mental hospital statistics are usually kept for administrative purposes. It is also necessary to ensure continuity of surveillance and administrative uniformity over a long period of time. This relatively rare situation obtained in one area to which we had access and one which, further, enjoys the signal advantage of having only one central psychiatric institution with a research-minded medical director, an excellent recording-system and a defined catchment-area with a population living in mixed urban and rural conditions.

Accordingly, it was possible to carry out a retrospective study of the outcome of two cohorts of all schizophrenics discharged from the hospital during 1967–68 and 1970–71 respectively.[5] The first period preceded the establishment of special clinics for the administration of long-acting drugs, the second followed their introduction. By comparing the numbers of patients readmitted and their length of time in hospital, therefore, we could obtain a crude index of the impact of the drugs on the movement of the schizophrenic population. The result of this analysis showed clearly that while fewer discharged schizophrenics were readmitted to hospital when on long-acting medication this advantage – if so it be construed – accrued only to those patients who, regardless of treatment, enjoyed a more favourable prognosis.

This method of inquiry is, of course, restricted to inferences drawn from information which excludes a central consideration, namely that even if a particular form of treatment were shown to facilitate discharge from hospital and maintenance in the community its importance could not be adequately assessed without reference to the subsequent quality of domestic life. The early studies of Pasamanick and his colleagues explicitly recognized the need to evaluate whether 'the mental hospital atmosphere is merely transferred to the home'.[6] In practical terms this entails the assessment of not only the patient's clinical status, including any adverse effects of medication, but also his social capacity, and the milieu in which he or she is supported. Information of this type can be obtained by direct observation within the framework of a therapeutic trial.

Against this background a comparative clinical trial of pimozide and fluphenazine decanoate was planned under the auspices of the MRC Drug Trials Committee in the early 1970s, with the aim of assessing the relative efficacy of the two compounds in the continuation therapy of patients returning to the community following hospitalization for an acute schizophrenic episode. The objectives were to ascertain:
1) the relapse and rate of relapse of schizophrenic symptomatology;
2) the frequency and severity of adverse effects;
3) the prevention of further admission to hospital;
4) the extra-mural social functioning of patients; and
5) the regularity of medication.
The details of this complex investigation have been published in full elsewhere[7, 8] and here I should like to concentrate merely on those aspects of the study with particular relevance to my theme.

First, the design and procedure. Over a period of nearly two years a careful assessment was made of all patients aged 17–60 with a suspected diagnosis of schizophrenia who were admitted to the one mental hospital providing psychiatric services to about 450,000 people. The population studied can therefore be regarded as a representative group of schizophrenics coming to medical attention. All patients underwent the Present State Examination and a diagnosis of 'definite' or 'probable' schizophrenia was made according to the symptomatic clinical picture in a standardized manner. Just before their discharge from hospital those patients included in the trial were allocated randomly to one of two medication regimes under double-blind conditions. In some measure, it may be observed, the design was heavily influenced by the Oedipus Effect, for the belief in the efficacy of neuroleptics delivered by the parenteral route was so firmly held by participating physicians with clinical responsibility that it proved impossible to induce them to agree to the administration of either an unsupported placebo or any form of oral medication alone.

Accordingly, the patients received either active pimozide tablets and inert fluphenazine-like injections, or the combination of active fluphenazine injections and inert pimozide-like tablets. A flexible drug-dosage was employed, the majority of patients receiving an average of 25mg fluphenazine fortnightly or 8mg pimozide daily. All trial medication was dispensed by a community nursing sister under psychiatric supervision at a follow-up clinic. Patients were asked to return tablet-containers and the riboflavin incorporated in all tablets made it possible to check further on drug-compliance by means of random urine-examinations. One month after discharge a clinical and a social assessment were made independently by means of the PSE and the Social Performance Schedule[9] administered respectively by a clinician and a social research worker, each trained in the use of these instruments, to the patients and their relatives or closest associates. Both assessments were repeated either 12 months after discharge, or earlier if the patient relapsed. Relapse was defined as a re-appearance or exacerbation of schizophrenic symptoms that led to withdrawal from the trial, whether or not it resulted in re-admission to hospital. Adverse effects were assessed at each clinical examination.

The results of this inquiry may be summarised under three categories: clinical and social outcome and adverse-effects:

1 Clinical outcome

There proved to be no significant difference between the proportion of patients on the two drug-regimes who relapsed with schizophrenic symptoms. Further, a survival curve indicated that there was no difference in the rate of relapse on the two drugs. All the relapses represented an exacerbation of persistent symptomatology, as assessed one month after discharge, rather than the reappearance of symptoms after an asymptomatic phase.

A more striking, because unsuspected, finding was the prominence of depressive symptomatology in the follow-up period. Depression turned out to be the most frequent cause of readmission to hospital, and more frequently than not it was unaccompanied by schizophrenic phenomena. Episodes of morbid depression were recorded of more than one-third of patients during the trial, and after one year the clinical picture was more frequently exhibited by patients on fluphenazine than by those receiving pimozide.

2 Social outcome

The indices employed to assess social disability were categorised separately as sociability and leisure activity, domestic relationships, heterosexual relationships, household-work and child-rearing, employment, burden on the family and overt behavioural disturbance. In general, the findings suggest that after one month and one year there was less social impairment among patients receiving pimozide.

3 Adverse effects

The pattern of adverse effects was similar for patients on both drugs, the most frequently recorded being extra-pyramidal symptoms, blurred vision, drowsiness and depressed mood. It may be noted, however, that the decreasing frequency of extra-pyramidal symptoms recorded among the pimozide-treated patients after 12 months was not observed among the patients receiving fluphenazine.

These findings indicate the importance of incorporating social as well as clinical measures in the assessment of outcome, since in this study, and subsequently in others, pimozide proved superior to phenothiazine preparations on various measures of social functioning. Why should this be the case? In pharmacodynamic terms the most usual explanation has been in terms of pimozide's comparative lack of sedative properties, but this was not supported by our data. Two other of its properties, however, may be more relevant. The first of these is the effect of psychomotor behaviour, by which I do not refer to the crude ambulatory activities which have been examined by other workers with negative results so much as the more subtle phenomena which play a part in non-verbal communication. Some evidence on this point was furnished by our finding reported 'rigidity' to be associated with impaired leisure activity and general sociability. Secondly, since a reduction in overt schizophrenic symptoms did not appear to be linked to reported social functioning of treated patients, the possible relationship to depressive symptoms must be taken into account.

For an adequate explanation of the findings exemplified by this study, however, it is necessary to consider more than drug action, for medication is clearly only one factor which determines the course of the condition. Several well-conducted studies have now shown that the course of schizophrenia is related to social as well as biological influences and that the interaction of these two modalities must be taken into account *ab initio*. Thus, for example, an impressive body of evidence has accumulated to show that schizophrenics tend both to avoid social contacts and to show a decrement of psychological functioning as social situations become more intense. Several workers have examined schizophrenics' adjustment in the community to find that contact with a relative who expresses a high degree of emotion is significantly associated with a high relapse rate.

A variety of reasons for this deleterious effects of social interaction on schizophrenics have been suggested, varying in content from the concepts of cognitive and non-cognitive psychology to the physiological vagaries of autonomic arousal. None is convincing. More to our concern, although continuation therapy with phenothiazines partially ameliorates the negative effect of extensive contact with an emotionally expressive relative, the negative effects of such interpersonal contact are also seen among patients receiving these drugs. Thus, in a recent NIMH study of the comparative effectiveness of injectable depot fluphenazine decanoate and oral fluphenazine hydrochloride, 28 per cent of the patients relapsed within their first year of community treatment.[10] Further, and contrary to the investigators' original hypothesis there were no significant differences between the efficacy of the two treatments, thus ruling out the widely held belief that phenothiazine treatment failures are primarily due to non-compliance on the part of the patient population. Instead, the findings indicated that phenothiazines by themselves do not necessarily permit schizophrenics to function at a level which will permit them to stay in the community. Further, since the symptoms of emotional withdrawal and blunted affect were more pronounced among patients who had not relapsed after one year in the community than they were in the beginning, although the prevalence of all other symptoms had decreased, it is suggested that some level of social withdrawal and non-involvement may be crucial for the schizophrenics' adjustment to their social environment.

In the light of such considerations the NIMH workers have gone so far as to maintain of schizophrenia that 'The development of successful treatment programmes may hinge on our learning more about the nature of this social dysfunction', regardless of its theoretical difficulties. This conclusion has, in fact, been accepted independently by Falloon, whose recent work in California has been concerned with family management in the prevention of schizophrenic relapses or exacerbations.[11] In a randomised, controlled study Falloon and his colleagues have compared the results of a family-treatment programme with individual supportive care in the community management of two groups of schizophrenics receiving long-term continuation drug-treatment. They have demonstrated the superiority of the former approach, which is based on an active attempt to 'enhance the stress-reducing capacity of the patient and the family through improved understanding of the illness and behavioural training'. Not the least interesting aspect of Falloon's conclusions is that the logical point of entry is the primary care system which is, of course, much more highly developed here than in North America. Further work along these lines, therefore, might profitably be pursued in this country.

The same might be expected *a fortiori* of those many other forms of mental disorder in which social factors exercise, if anything, an even more potent influence than they do on schizophrenia. In tackling the problems of therapeutic evaluation in such conditions the clinical investigator must remain aware of John Ryle's distinction between disease in man and man in disease. I hope that awareness is now spreading to the pharmaceutical industry.

REFERENCES

1 Maudsley H (1879): *The Pathology of Mind*. Macmillan: London.
2 Shepherd M (1980): 'From social medicine to social psychiatry'. *Psychological Medicine*, 10, 211–18.
3 Bourne H (1953): 'The insulin myth'. *Lancet*, 7 November 1953, 964–8.

4 Shepherd M (1959): 'The social outcome of early schizophrenia'. *Psychiatria et Neurologia*, 137, No 4, 224–9.

5 Shepherd M and Watt D C (1975): 'Impact of long-term neuroleptics on the community: advantages and disadvantages'. In *Neuropsychopharmacology*, edited by Boissier J R, Hippius H and Pichot P, Elsevier: New York.

6 Pasamanick B, Scarpetti F R, and Dinitz S (1967): *Schizophrenics in the Community*. Appleton Century-Crofts: New York.

7 Falloon I, Watt D C and Shepherd M (1978): 'A comparative controlled trial of pimozide and fluphenazine decanoate in the continuation therapy of schizophrenia'. *Psychological Medicine*, 8, 59–70.

8 Falloon I, Watt D C and Shepherd M (1978): 'The social outcome of patients in a trial of long-term continuation therapy in schizophrenia: pimozide vs. fluphenazine'. *Psychological Medicine*, 8, 256–74.

9 Stevens B (1972): 'Dependence of schizophrenic patients on elderly relatives'. *Psychological Medicine*, 2, 17–32.

10 Schooler C and Spohn H E (1982): 'Social dysfunction and treatment failure in schizophrenia'. *Schizophrenia Bulletin*, 8, No 1, 85–98.

11 Falloon I R H, Boyd J L, McGill C W, Razani J, Moss H B and Gilderman A M (1982): 'Family management in the prevention of exacerbations of schizophrenia: a controlled study'. *New England Journal of Medicine*, 306, 1437–40.

Measurement of the benefits of benzodiazepines

John Marks
Cambridge University

The ultimate aim of measurement is to be able to compare findings in objective, numeric terms. Unfortunately it is not yet possible to express the benefit of many forms of therapy in such objective numeric terms and the use of psychotropic drugs is among those that *currently* falls into this category.

For example, therapy may be life improving not life saving, influencing the quality of life of the individual. To express the subjective features of quality of life in objective terms has until very recently been beyond the current state of the economic art. The whole concept of 'health indicators' is a recent one and has not yet been applied to a study of the benzodiazepines. Hopefully, as a result of current interest, such methods will become both accepted and used.

Until such time as they do become both available and accepted it is necessary to express such benefit in qualitative rather than quantitative terms and to try to compare alternative forms of therapy in such terms, even though the accuracy is restricted. Hard data on the social aspects are hard to find and economists will unfortunately find this presentation less than ideal; but it represents the state of the art as currently applied to the benzodiazepines.

Nevertheless, despite the difficulties, there is a need to define therapeutic benefit. All forms of treatment use scarce resources and these must be used to the best advantage. This implies that an attempt must be made to assess the relative benefits of various forms of therapy not only for the individual but for society.

The other difficulty is that the results of all forms of therapy consist of a balance between benefit and problems. Hence it is necessary to measure both the benefits and the disadvantages of any form of therapy.

Even when it becomes possible to express much of the information in quantitative terms there will still, in my opinion, be three stages of investigation before the overall benefit of any therapy can be determined, viz:

1 Measurement of medical benefit
2 Measurement of social and moral issues
3 Measurement of economic aspects.

These three stages will be demonstrated by considering the example of the benzodiazepines.

The benzodiazepine class of substance is a therapeutic group that is reputed to be amongst the most widely prescribed of any.[1,2] Moreover since members of the group have now been available in clinical study and therapeutic use for about a quarter of a century there should have been full opportunity for the benefit to be assessed. It is therefore all the more surprising that despite the 25 years of continuous study and widespread use, there is still dispute[3] about the overall value of this therapeutic group. This indicates the difficulty of evaluating benefit save in the exceptional circumstances of life saving drugs.

The measurement of medical benefit and risk

Confirmation of medical benefit is the logical starting point, for without this other considerations become pointless. This involves the consideration of the balance between therapeutic activity and adverse reactions.

Judgement of therapeutic activity comes first from the results of clinical trials and subsequently from the appraisal by the clinician in practice. Both stages are essential, for they give complementary information. The clinical trials should determine not only the level of activity and the incidence of adverse reactions but also compare the activity with that achieved with alternative and preferably standard forms of therapy. This information will come serially from uncontrolled dose ranging trials and subsequent adequately controlled blind clinical trials. Although there is no dispute about the need for double blind controlled studies there is great value in the observations of those who are experienced in the field, and the use of controlled trials at too early a stage in the study of a new substance may well be counter-productive.[4] It is clearly outside the remit of this paper to consider the clinical studies in detail. Suffice it to say that the aim must be to select relevant tests and make them as objective as possible.[5] In the field of the study of psychotherapeutic agents much of the information perforce comes in the form of subjective appraisals of symptoms by the patient and it is now considered that the use of visual analogue scales gives the most simple and reliable results.

It must be noted however that the benzodiazepines have many widely varied uses and that the assessment of the value in these various uses may be different. In order to attempt to quantify the value in each therapeutic indication it is desirable to indicate the life-threatening nature of the disorder, or the social cost of the disease if it is not life threatening; the level of therapeutic benefit achieved, and the availability of alternative forms of therapy (Table 1). A semi-quantitative approach is in my opinion all that is currently feasible.

This table indicates clearly that when the techniques of medical economics are applied to the study of the benzodiazepines it will not be sufficient to determine the benefit in one indication but in a series of which those shown in Table 1 are only representative examples. Thus for example the use in muscle spasms covers many different forms of disease while for simplicity the broad use in anaesthesia has been omitted from this list.

The medical assessment also involves the measurement of the adverse reactions. These can be measured in terms of mortality and morbidity.

In the case of mortality Greenblatt and Shader in their masterly monograph on the benzodiazepines in 1974[2] wrote: 'in the medical literature there are no reported cases of fatal overdosage due to the benzodiazepines alone'. Nine years later, with further experience, this is still probably very close to the truth.

To attempt to measure the risk arising from drug overdosage it is necessary to undertake large surveys.[6-9] In one of the best of these Finkle et al[7] examined 1,500 drug fatalities from a survey of 24 major cities in the United

TABLE 1 **Variation in therapeutic benefit of the benzodiazepines depending upon the indication.**

Disorder	Cost of Disorder	Therap Benefit*	Alternatives
Anxiety	Social cost ++	50%	Several
Insomnia	Social cost +	60%	Several
Muscle spasms	Social cost +	60%	Several
Status epilepticus	Life threatening	80%	Few
Tetanus	Life threatening	90%	Few

*in excess of response to placebo

States and three Provinces of Canada. The combined population totalled some 79.2 million people and the study covered a $3\frac{1}{2}$ year period between 1973 and 1976. In only two cases, one in the United States and one in Canada was a benzodiazepine alone found to be present.

Hence mortality from overdosage of benzodiazepines alone is extremely rare. The level can be expressed in quantitative terms for information on the size of the community involved in the study can readily be converted into the numbers at risk.

So far as tissue and organ toxicity are concerned there have been two extensive studies of the benzodiazepines.[10, 11] These studies indicated that the overall incidence of unwanted effects is low, indeed scarcely above the level found with placebo; that most are dose related and disappear rapidly with dose reduction and that virtually no important adverse reactions occur with benzodiazepines.

The only real medical problem with the benzodiazepines, a problem which they share with most other central nervous system active drugs, is the possible development of dependence.

Since the original studies by Hollister,[12] it has been known that the benzodiazepines when given in high doses could produce physical dependence. A survey of the world literature from 1960 to 1977 tried to express the risk in quantitative terms. It showed[13] that the incidence of *published cases* was low, that most were associated with mixed drug abuse, occurred in so-called 'dependence-prone' individuals[14, 15] and that they involved high daily dosage and prolonged administration. A recent[16] update of this survey of the world literature confirmed these factors and on the basis of eight prospective studies tried to quantify the *true risk* with continuous administration of therapeutic doses as opposed to the incidence of published cases and found it to be low when the benzodiazepines are used for periods less than about 3–4 months. Prolonged *continuous* use carries a substantial risk of dependence particularly in those with a predisposition to dependence as shown by the concurrent overuse of alcohol for example. Elsewhere the clinical significance of this risk[16] is assessed. From the point of view of the measurement of benefit, the important point is to appreciate that the benefit will be determined to be different depending upon whether the benzodiazepine is being used correctly to just cover the periods of acute distress or misused as long term suppressive therapy without medical justification.

A third aspect of morbidity which must be examined for any psycho-

TABLE 2 **Appraisal of the balance of benefit with various agents (medical and social) for the relief of secondary anxiety.**

	Benzodiazepines	Barbiturates	Alcohol	Smoking
Therapeutic Value/breadth	+++	++	+	−
Mortality	±	++	+++	+++
Morbidity	±	+	++	++
Dependence	+	++	++	+
Performance deficit	+	++	+++	−

active substance is its influence on the handling of dangerous equipment and particularly car driving.

The vast majority of studies which attempt to examine the effect of psychotropic medication on driving ability, make two cardinal errors: they are carried out in normal volunteers, not a population of patients and they make use of so-called 'skills related to driving' rather than actual driving performance under natural conditions. The first of these factors has been shown to be of paramount importance, since the effect of illness, personality, sex, age and physical condition, on driving ability is large enough to outweigh drug effects.[17–20] In fact, there is evidence that in some individuals, a tranquilliser may correct adverse effects of emotional disturbance on driving ability.[21]

The available methodology also has severe limitations:[22] performance on the simulator, even when this closely resembles a real vehicle, correlates poorly with observed driving performance of the same individuals:[23] results of performance tests using single items or batteries are conflicting.[19,24,25]

Hence though prudence requires that patients be made aware that their performance may be impaired, we must accept that there is no current method of quantifying the impairment or even being sure that it exists.

On the basis of all the evidence we can examine the overall balance of the medical benefit qualitatively and conclude that the balance is heavily in favour of the benzodiazepines (Table 2). For comparison some other medical and social methods of relieving anxiety are included. The significance of this comparison will be considered later.

The measurement of social and moral issues

The mere finding of medical benefit does not imply social benefit if the substance is unnecessary, overused, or leads to social problems and this has been claimed to be the situation for the benzodiazepines particularly in relation to their use in the relief of anxiety.

Anxiety can exist as a primary disease, but this is a rare phenomenon. The anxiety which forms the major part of the work load in the practitioner's surgery is a secondary anxiety which stems from a variety of environmental factors. For some it may be an unsatisfactory home, for some promotion to too high a level of incompetence at work, but for many, the dole queue will be one of the important factors.

Clearly the best answer would be to remove all these social and domestic ills. To remove them is however rather akin to a task of Hercules, except perhaps in Utopia. And even if we could remove all the social ills we would still encounter the anxiety associated with physical ills.

We must therefore, perforce, take a pragmatic approach over the question of symptomatic relief of anxiety, while satisfying ourselves that we do not hinder the search for social cures for the problems.

The first social aspect for attention is whether the level of use is justified. There was a compound increase of use of the benzodiazepines from their introduction in 1960 to 1975 of about 2 per cent per year in the United Kingdom.[13] A factor in this growth was their substitution for the less effective and more dangerous barbiturates. In most countries the level reached a maximum during the mid 1970s. In many the level of use has declined since then.[26] Measured in terms of defined daily dosage (DDD) – the criterion recommended by WHO – the use levels out rather uniformly from one country to another.

The level of use can also be defined by the proportion of the population that is receiving the drug. This may be the proportion that have used the drug over a defined period (often the past year) or the point prevalence of use. The former clearly gives significantly higher figures than the latter depending upon the length of the period over which the incidence is determined.

In the early 1970s,[27,28] in several countries in Europe and the USA,[27] between 10 and 17 per cent of the population had used tranquillo-sedatives during the previous year with a regular use between 3 and 8 per cent. Benzodiazepines represented about 60 per cent of this use. Mellinger and Balter have recently updated (1979) the figures for the United States.[29] These comparative figures, with a gap of almost a decade, confirm that the level of use has indeed fallen.

From various studies we also know that women are prescribed tranquillisers about twice as frequently as men and that the elderly are higher users than the young.[1,26,29]

Several recent studies have shown an annual level of significant psychiatric morbidity in the population of developed countries of about 30 per cent and a point prevelance of about 15 per cent. Of this morbid anxiety accounts for the major share.[30] Hence the current level of prescription of tranquillo-sedatives (annual level about 10 per cent) is low rather than high compared with this level of morbidity and does not suggest inappropriate prescribing.

However, the finding that the proportion who receive a group of drugs corresponds to the proportion suffering from the equivalent disorder does not indicate that the correct patients are being treated. However, evidence of valid use is available for the tranquillisers. Uhlenhuth et al[31] showed that the level of tranquilliser use correlated well with the level of anxiety, while Hesbacher et al[32] in over 1,000 people in a general practice found a very good 'illness-treatment fit'; ie 99.1 per cent of patients having no emotional disorders had never received tranquillisers while of those diagnosed as suffering from emotional illness, less than half had been treated with psychoactive drugs. In a further study which compared medication use and psychic distress, virtually all the regular users of psychotherapeutic drugs reported psychic distress or life crises. On the other hand, of those reporting both a high level of emotional distress and life crises only 35 per cent of the women and 21 per cent of the men had used any psychoactive medication at any time in the previous year[33] again suggesting underuse rather than the reverse.

TABLE 3 **Comparison of the effects of diazepam with other medications in the workplace.**[38]

	Number	Accidents	Days absent	Performance*
No medication	581	0.11 (0.34)	5.60 (6.09)	3.45 (0.83)
Non psychoactive	114	0.10 (0.30)	8.24 (8.53)	3.36 (0.74)
Other psychoactive	−28	0.21 (0.41)	10.60 (10.89)	3.14 (0.80)
Diazepam	39	0.12 (0.40)	9.87 (12.97)	3.51 (0.79)

*Higher score indicates superior performance.
The figures are shown as means and standard denotions.

This still leaves open the question of the higher use of tranquillisers by women[29, 34]. The total cause for this is not yet explained[34,35] but the evidence all suggests that the higher use is justified.[16] This despite the fact that sociologists have claimed that people are being prescribed drugs which they do not need[36] and that social solutions are not being sought.[3,37]

Two recent studies have examined the social aspects of benzodiazepine use. The first compared diazepam with other non-psychotropic medicines in the work setting[38] (Table 3). Diazepam was not associated with any difference from the other medicines in accident rate, absentee rate or performance. The second study was based on questionnaires from 389 prescribing physicians and 366 psychologists and social workers. No less than 92 per cent perceived tranquillisers as having the potential for improving the general quality of life.[39] This contrasts with the perception of benefit of stimulants of 41 per cent, barbiturates 36 per cent and alcohol only 22 per cent.

The evidence in the United Kingdom is that tranquillisers are not being given for social ills,[40] while studies in the United States[28,41] indicated a sensible and realistic approach to the use of these drugs. For example, while 77 per cent perceived diazepam to be effective, 69 per cent were well aware that tranquillisers 'do not get at underlying problems' and 46 per cent had reservations about tranquilliser use.

The implications of the use of tranquillisers must be viewed against the social alternatives for stress management. In males it is known that alcohol may be used as a form of self medication[42,43] alternative to the tranquillisers. Thus in Finland for example, as the use of psychotropic drugs fell, reputedly due to altered prescribing procedures, there was a coincident rise in the consumption of alcohol,[44] though there may be alternative explanations for the association other than substitution.

There is moreover no evidence that if benzodiazepines are not administered, the patients either seek out a social solution to their problems or recover more rapidly. The concept that the administration of benzodiazepines retards social solutions might be more acceptable if social solutions were available. As Mellinger[45] has pointed out, those in distress who are refused treatment seek solace elsewhere and 'society often does not provide a great deal in the way of viable alternatives that are much better'. Hence there is no evidence that the administration of benzodiazepines retards the search for social solutions.

The other social concern about any psychoactive substance in the risk of abuse. Benzodiazepines are indeed encountered in the street drug abuse scene in most countries, usually as part of the common pattern of mixed drug abuse. Navaratnam[46] has tried to quantify the level of benzodiazepine abuse and, on the basis of current evidence, has found it low. This is consistent with the low preference rating of benzodiazepines in the drug abuse scene.[15] However as Smith[15] has stressed, whereas narcotics are drugs of primary abuse benzodiazepines are only rarely so and do not usually increase social problems.

Hence there is little evidence of undesirable sociological consequences from the current availability and use of benzodiazepines.

However, it will be clear that in the context of social benefit, studies are in their infancy and valid techniques for quantifying such studies are urgently needed. The definition of appropriate health indicators and examination of how to quantify them (perhaps by some form of visual analogue scale technique) would help to secure the relevant information in a more quantitive form.

The cost benefit balance for the benzodiazepines

At the present time, and despite recent developments, the science of cost/benefit or cost/effectiveness analysis is still in its infancy and there are virtually no studies that have examined the situation for the psychoactive drugs – let alone the benzodiazepines.

We can of course see what are the alternatives and determine their cost. If tranquillisers are not given then the patient may turn to the alternatives of alcohol[42,43] or tobacco. From the benefit/toxicity viewpoint these show a very poor picture compared to the benzodiazepines.[13]

This can be extended to examine the cost of treatment with the benzodiazepines as opposed to the alternatives (Table 4). A comparison is made of the daily costs of the possible alternative strategies for the relief of a moderate anxiety such as is seen daily by the practitioner. There are serious difficulties in expressing anything like equivalent activity, but the difference in cost is so obvious that minor differences about equivalence of effects is not going to seriously affect the answer.

The real answer to much of the secondary anxiety is the modification of the unacceptable environment that is the prime cause. However, no attempt has been made to express the cost of this in the table. A team composed of a sociologist and an economist may be able to provide the daily

TABLE 4 **The cost of treatment with benzodiazepines compared with alternatives.**

	£ per day
Benzodiazepine	0.05
Alcohol (6 tots)	1.00
Cigarettes (10)	0.70
Psychotherapy (2 sessions per week)	3.00
Social change	?

TABLE 5   **Suggested substitutes for treatment with psychotropic agents.**[47]

If no tranquillizers were available . . .	Frequency of mentions in % (N = 657)
Longer medical consultations would be needed	75.3
The patient would visit the doctor more frequently	72.1
Psychotherapy would be required	62.4
Patient would need a period in a sanatorium	52.1
Patient could turn to alcohol	50.7
Patient would require so much attention in the practice that treatment of other patients could suffer	46.9
Patient would use preparations not recommended by doctor to treat organic complaints	44.0
Patient would need to be hospitalized	38.7
Patient would use addictive drugs	36.5
Patient would have to be treated with medicaments which could be used to commit suicide	34.4

Source   See Reference 47.

cost which we the population would have to pay. Even leaving aside the fact that the cost is likely to be large, no political structure anywhere in the world, whatever its colour, has yet been able to achieve it. WHO surveys have indicated that the level of anxiety is uniformly high whether the country is rich or poor, North or South, industrially developed or rural. Thus, while we may agree with sociologists that the ultimate answer lies in social adjustment, from the practical point of view we must conclude that until there is a new approach to the social problems of humanity, mankind will search for a chemical relief for his worries.

Other possible substitutes for the tranquillisers were determined in a study with 657 doctors in Germany[47] (Table 5). When the costs of the doctors' time, the costs of psychotherapy and/or the costs of hospitalisation are calculated, it is apparent that the loss of availability of psychotropic drugs could not be adequately compensated for by the alternative methods or only at greater cost.

But supposing we attempt to determine the benefit/cost directly. Although we can express the costs of treatment in financial terms with a reasonable level of reliability we cannot yet express all the benefits in similar terms. We can, of course, determine the reduction in the period away from work that can be achieved with therapy. We can express the increase in the earning power achieved with a better health record. What we cannot yet express in monetary terms is the level of physical and social well-being in the field of secondary anxiety, by some form of health indicator, even if we had a good method for determining the extent to which our existing health level was below the ideal. Not least of our problems in this respect is that one person will make light of their major physical or mental disabilities while another will be prostrate with a minor disorder.

However, one study on the value of tranquillisers has been attempted – in Germany in 1972.[48] The author concluded that if no increased use of hospitals resulted from the total withdrawal of tranquillisers, then the saving made by prescribing them was of the order of 1,846 million DM. If a high level of hospital use resulted from the withdrawal of tranquillisers then they calculated that the figure would rise to about 15,000 million DM.

In detailed terms this study can be criticised. Nevertheless it is the first attempt to measure the social benefit of tranquillisers to the community and shows that the benefit is substantial, measured in monetary terms.

Conclusions

We may conclude that to measure benefits three stages of assessment are necessary.
1 Medical benefits
2 Social aspects
3 Cost/benefit analysis.

At each stage we must note that there is a balance between pro and contra aspects and both of these must be put into the equation.

It is apparent that while we can define a lot of the benefits in qualitative and even semi-quantitative terms very little has yet been expressed in true quantitative form. This is clearly an area in which there is considerable possibilities for further work.

More than any other aspect, it is apparent that the measurement of the economic benefit of the benzodiazepines involves not one single estimation but an appraisal of their benefit in each of their many therapeutic indications. When efforts are made to measure the social benefits in a more quantitative fashion it is important to appreciate that one of the most important factors in the assessment is to ensure that the benzodiazepines are being used in a medically appropriate fashion ie to cover periods of emotional distress.

Even when such studies are feasible it is apparent that there will be some areas in which value judgements have to be made. In the meantime, bear-

FIGURE 1 **Qualitative overall assessment of the benefits of the benzodiazepines.**

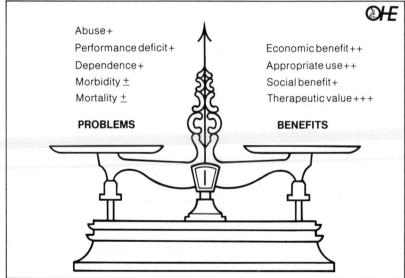

ing in mind the inherent difficulties, it is possible to summarise the total balance in at least a semi-quantitative form (Figure 1). This shows the benzo-diazepines are as Lader concludes[1] 'far more beneficial than harmful'.

REFERENCES

1 Lader M H, The present status of benzodiazepines in psychiatry and medicine, *Arzneim-Forsch*, *30*, 910–912 (1980).

2 Greenblatt D J, Shader R I, Benzodiazepines in Clinical Practice, Raven Press, New York, (1974).

3 Cooperstock R, Psychotropic drug use among women, *Can Med Ass J*, *115*, 760–763 (1976).

4 Marks J, Placebomania, *J New Drugs*, *2*, 71–77 (1962).

5 Matz R S, Nash R J, Clinical evaluation of anxiolytic drugs, Anxiolytics. Eds. Fielding S, Lal H, Futura Publ. New York, pp 247–280 (1979).

6 Lawson A A H, Mitchell I, Patients with acute poisoning seen in a general medical unit (1960–1971), *Brit Med J*, *4*, 153–154 (1971).

7 Finkle B S, McCloskey K L, Goodman L S, Diazepam and drug associated deaths: a United States and Canadian survey, *J Amer Med Ass*, *242*, 429–434 (1979).

8 Myers J B, Smith A J, Elliott R L, Macaskill P, Self poisoning with drugs: a $3\frac{1}{2}$ year study in Newcastle, N.S.W., *Med J Aust*, *2*, 402–405 (1981).

9 Volans G N, The poisons unit experience, In: Murray J, *et al*, Eds., The Misuse of Psycho-tropic Drugs, Gaskell, Roy Coll Psychiat (1981).

10 Svenson S E, Hamilton R G, A critique of overemphasis on side effects with the psycho-tropic drugs: an analysis of 18,000 chlordiazepoxide treated cases, *Curr Ther Res*, *8*, 455–464 (1966).

11 Boston Collaborative Drug Surveillance Program: clinical depression of the central nervous system due to diazepam and chlordiazepoxide in relation to cigarette smoking and age, *New Eng J Med*, *288*, 277–280 (1973).

12 Hollister L E, Motzenbecker F P, Degan R O, Withdrawal reactions from chlordiazepoxide (Librium), *Psychopharmacologia*, *2*, 63–68 (1961).

13 Marks J, The benzodiazepines: use, overuse, misuse, abuse?, Lancaster: MTP Press, (1978).

14 Hollister L E, Ed. Valium. A discussion of current issues, *Psychosomatics*, *18*, 44–58 (1977).

15 Smith D, Dept of Health and Human Serv Publ Health Serv, Food and Drug Admin, Drug Abuse Advis Comm, Transcript of hearing, 14th May 1981. Rockville, Maryland, USA.

16 Marks J, The benzodiazepines – an international perspective, *J Psychoactive Drugs*, (1983, in press).

17 Clayton A B, Betts T A, Harvey P G, The influence of sex and personality factors upon the effect of tranquillisers on driving performanc In: Israelstam S, Lambert S (eds) Proc 6th Int Conf on Alcohol, Drugs and Traffic Safety. Addiction Res Found, Toronto, Ontario, Canada, pp 415–422 (1975).

18 Honkanen R, Ertama L, Linnoila M, Alha A, Lukkari I, Karlsson M, Diviluoto O, Puro M, Role of drugs in traffic accidents, *Brit Med J*, *281*, 1309–1312 (1980).

19 Kleinknecht R A, Donaldson D, A review of the effects of diazepam on cognitive and psychomotor performance, *J Nerv Ment Dis*, *161*, 399–411 (1975).

20 Linnoila M, Liljequist R, Olkoniemi J, *et al*, Effect of alcohol and benzodiazepines on per-formance as related to personality characteristics. Personality characteristics among healthy 'placebo reactors' and nonreactors, *Pharmakopsychiatrie*, 10, 246–253 (1977).

21 Landauer A A, Diazepam and traffic accidents, *Brit Med J*, *2*, 209 (1981).

22 Vogel J R, Objective measurement of human performance changes produced by anti-anxiety drugs, In: Anxiolytics. Eds Fielding S, Lal H, Futura Publ. New York, pp 343–374 (1979).

23 Edwards D S, Hahn C P, Fleishmann E A, Evaluation of laboratory methods for the study of driving behaviour. The relation between simulator and street performance, Amer Inst Research Rep. R 69/7 Washington, (1969).

24 Linnoila M, Psychomotor effects of drugs and alcohol on healthy volunteers and psychiatric patients, *Adv Pharmacol Ther*, *8*, 235–249 (1978).

25 Landauer A A, Diazepam and driving ability, Med J Austr, *68*, 624–626 (1981).

26 Marks J, L'utilisation therapeutique de tranquillisants dans le monde, *Rev Prat*, *32*, 2897–2908 (1982).

K

27 Balter M B, Levine J, Manheimer D I, Cross-national study of the extent of anti-anxiety/ sedative drug use, *New Engl J Med, 290*, 769–774 (1974).

28 Parry H J, Balter M B, Mellinger G D, Cisin I H, *et al*, National patterns of psychotherapeutic drug use, *Arch Gen Psychiatry, 28*, 769–784 (1973).

29 Mellinger G D, Balter M B, Prevalence and patterns of use of psychotherapeutic drugs; results from a 1979 national survey of American adults, Paper, International seminar on the epidemiological impact of psycho-tropic drugs, Milan, 24–26th June (1981).

30 Marks J, The benzodiazepines – use and abuse, Arzniem-Forsch, *30*, 898–901 (1981).

31 Uhlenheth E H, Balter M B, Lipman R S, Minor tranquillizers: clinical correlates of use in an urban population, *Arch Gen Psychiatry, 35*, 650–655 (1978).

32 Hesbacher P, Stepansky P, Stepansky E, Rickels K, Psychotropic drug use in family practice, *Pharmako-psychiatry Neuropsychopharmakol, 9*, 50–60 (1976).

33 Mellinger G D, Balter M B, Manheimer D I, Cisin I H, Parry H-J, Psychic distress, life crisis and the use of psychotherapeutic medications, *Arch Gen Psychiatry, 35*, 1045–1052 (1978).

34 Bass M J, Do physicians overprescribe for women with emotional problems? *Canad Med Ass J, 125*, 1211 (1981).

35 Roskies E, Sex, culture and illness – an overview, *Soc Sci Med, 12b*, 139–144 (1978).

36 Twaddle A C, Sweet R ·H, Characteristics and experiences of patients with preventable hospital admission, *Soc Sci Med, 4*, 141–145 (1970).

37 Koumjian K, The use of Valium as a form of social control, *Soc Sci Med, 15e*, 245–249 (1981).

38 Proctor R C, Prescription medication in the workplace, *North Carolina Med J, 42*, 545–547 (1981).

39 Whybrow P C, Matlins S M, Greenberg M D, The social impact of psychotropic drugs – perceptions of prescribing and non-prescribing health practitioners. (In press).

40 Williams P, Murray J, Clare A, A longitudinal study of psychotropic drug prescription, *Psychol Med, 12*, 201–206 (1982).

41 Tessler R, Stokes R, Pietras M, Consumer response to Valium. A survey of attitudes and patterns of use, *Drug Therapy, 8*, 179–186 (1978).

42 Manheimer D D, Davidson S T, Balter M B, Popular attitudes and beliefs about tranquilizers, *Amer J Psychiatry, 130*, 1246–1253 (1973).

43 Parry H J, Cisin I H, Balter M B, *et al*, Increased alcohol intake as a coping mechanism for psychic distress, In Cooperstock R, Ed, Social aspects of the medical use of psychotropic drugs, Addiction Research Foundation, Ottawa, (1974).

44 Idanpaan-Heikkila J, Studies in drug utilisation, WHO Regional Publications European Series No 8, Copenhagen WHO, (1979).

45 Mellinger G D, Use of licit drugs and other coping alternatives: some personal observations on the hazards of living. In: Drugs and Suicide – when other coping strategies fail. Lettiere D J, Ed. Sage Publications, Beverly Hills, (1978).

46 Navaratnam V, Impact of scheduling drugs under the 1971 Convention on Psychotropic Substances – the benzodiazepines reappraised, National Drug Research Centre, Pulau Pinang, Malaysia. (1983).

47 Contest: Psychopharmaka – Arztebefragung, Volume of Statistics. Frankfurt on Main (1974).

48 Psychotropic drugs – economically considered (a cost benefit analysis of the use of tranquilizers in the Federal Republic of Germany in 1972), Basle Socioeconomic Studies No 4 (1974).

A government economist's attitudes to the new measures*

Jeremy Hurst
Department of Health and Social Security

Introduction
My attitude to health status measurement contains elements of both caution and enthusiasm.

Enthusiasm
Let me start, in an uncharacteristic Civil Service fashion, with the enthusiasm. Earlier papers in this volume have stressed that health economists are committed to the search for ways of improving the allocation of resources in the health field. This search is severely handicapped by the lack of an accepted measure of the benefits or yield from health expenditure. There has, of course, been some use of indicators of outcome in evaluations of drugs and other treatments but we have seen that, usually, these deal with only some aspects of health – such as mortality or return to work – and they are most often used in a tactical sense to compare one version of a particular therapy for a particular condition with another (or with a placebo) rather than in a strategic sense to compare different therapies for a given condition or perhaps different therapies for different conditions. This means that considerable ambiguity persists about the relative value of different health service activities.

Illustrative use of a full measure of health status for NHS *resource allocation purposes*
Comprehensive measurement of health status, of the kind described in earlier papers in this volume, offers a sharp reduction in ambiguity about the value of health service activities. It should provide the opportunity to bring about a better allocation of resources. The picture I have in mind is of being able to weigh the costs of treatment against the benefits of treatment to arrive at more rational decisions. Let me illustrate, drawing on one of the measures described earlier in this volume and on some cost data gathered recently by the Economic Advisers' Office in DHSS. My illustration will be an example of 'cost-utility analysis' according to the classification of appraisals adopted in the chapter by Mike Drummond.

Table 1 shows 'A Scale of Valuation of states of illness for 70 patients, nurses, doctors and health volunteers' devised by Rachel Rosser and Paul Kind.[1] It may be particularly appropriate to quote their experimental work because it was done with the help of DHSS sponsorship. Health was described along two dimensions – disability (8 states) and distress (4 states).

*The remarks in this paper are personal in origin and do not necessarily reflect official thinking in the DHSS. I am grateful for comments, on an earlier version of this paper, from Dr G M Cochrane, Mr J D Pole and Dr R Rosser. They are, of course, not responsible for any remaining shortcomings. The content of this paper is Crown Copyright ©.

TABLE 1   **A scale of valuation of states of illness for 70 patients, nurses, doctors and healthy volunteers**

| | *Distress state* | | | |
Disability state	*None*	*Mild*	*Moderate*	*Severe*
None	0.00	1.00	2.00	6.67
Slight social	2.00	2.70	5.45	13.50
Severe social or slight work impairment	4.00	5.53	8.75	17.50
Severe work or housework impairment	7.25	8.70	11.67	26.00
Unable to work or mainly confined to home	10.85	13.03	20.00	60.00
Confined to chair or wheelchair	25.00	31.00	64.00	200.00
Confined to bed	64.50	87.20	200.00	497.14
Unconscious	405.71			

Note   When scale refers to permanent states, score for death is 200.
Source   Adapted from Rosser and Kind, *Inter Journal of Epidemiology*, Vol 7 No 4.

Each subject was asked to compare each state for severity during a carefully structured interview. Examples of states were: 'can work normally, do everything at home and have a normal social life. In moderate pain which is not relieved by aspirin'; and 'can only move around in a wheelchair. Has slight pain which is relieved by aspirin.' Patients were later asked to include death on the scale when states were considered as permanent. It was made clear that what was wanted was a ratio scale – that is for each health state a ratio was required which would: either define the proportion of resources that each subject considered it was justifiable to allocate for the relief of a person in the more severe state compared with the less ill; or define the subject's point of indifference between curing one of the iller people or a number (specified by the ratio) of less ill people. The results of this study and of more recent work suggest strongly that it is indeed possible to produce a ratio scale for measuring severity of illness. The values reproduced in Figure 1 represent the median values for 70 participants (there were wide differences in values between individuals, of course). An interesting feature of this scale is that there are two permanent states judged (on average) to be worse than death – 'unconscious' and 'confined to bed and in severe distress'.

Table 2 shows the approximate cost to the NHS (only) of treatment of some selected conditions: 1 year's haemodialysis at home; perpetual treatment on haemodialysis, assuming a 5 per cent per annum discount rate; a successful kidney transplant followed by maintenance therapy; and herniotomy in an NHS hospital (all at November 1981 prices). These are drawn from recent studies by my colleague Peter Mancini, in the Economic Advisers' Office. In a full evaluation private sector costs would be measured, also.

It is possible, for illustrative purposes, to speculate about how such sets of information might be combined to aid decisions on resource allocation. Supposing that investigation revealed that haemodialysis put patients with chronic renal failure, on average, in a state involving 'severe social or slight

TABLE 2 **Costs of selected treatments provided by the NHS (£ at November 1981 prices)**

1 year's haemodialysis (at home)	8,000
Haemodialysis (at home) to perpetuity discounted at 5 per cent per annum	160,000
Successful kidney transplant followed by maintenance therapy discounted at 5 per cent per annum	35,000
Uncomplicated Herniotomy	420

work impairment' and 'moderate distress' and (of course) averted death. Then the gain in health status according to the Rosser/Kind index would be 200.00–8.75 = 191.25. Similarly, if a successful kidney transplant (with subsequent maintenance) took individuals, on average, to a state involving 'slight social' disability and 'mild' distress and averted death, the gain in health status would be 200.00–2.70 = 197.30. Lastly, if herniotomy (without complications) took individuals on average from a state involving 'severe social or slight work impairment' and 'mild' distress to a state involving no disability or distress, then the gain in health status would be 5.53–0.00 = 5.53.

The yield in health status from each treatment could then be divided by the cost of each treatment to provide estimates of 'health status yield per £'. Table 3 shows the results of such calculations. In this (purely illustrative) example uncomplicated herniotomy comes out as better value than a successful kidney transplant and a successful kidney transplant as better value than home haemodialysis. Of course, even if we had reliable information of this type, it would not be enough to allow us to conclude immediately that, say, fewer patients should be dialysed and more given hernia repairs. The figures which are illustrated give average values for benefits and costs. It is likely that marginal costs are higher and marginal benefits lower for each condition. The marginal benefit for hernia repair may be well below average benefit if all potential patients are being offered surgery (after a certain waiting time) whereas the marginal benefit for renal dialysis may be quite close to the average benefit if kidney machines are in short supply. As for renal transplantation, there are constraints on the rate of transplantation because of shortages of donated kidneys. Moreover, a proper estimate of the cost and gain from transplantation would take account of the risk of an unsuccessful outcome.

Nevertheless, supposing that valid calculations of this kind could be made across the full range of treatments, and that these were properly interpreted with supporting information, then they would surely transform the debate about the relative merits of extra spending, at the margin, on

TABLE 3 **Illustrative health status yield per £ for selected treatments provided by the NHS**

	Health status yield	Cost £	Health status yield per £,000
Home haemodialysis	191.25	160,000	1.2
Successful kidney transplant with subsequent maintenance	197.30	35,000	5.6
Uncomplicated herniotomy	5.53	420	13.2

each of the activities which compete for a limited NHS budget. Health economists would be particularly enthusiastic if the techniques brought better information about consumers' perceptions and valuations of health states to bear on NHS decisions.

The approach would be valid, in principle, for evaluating drugs and for comparing drug treatments with other treatments. The case for more comprehensive economic evaluation of drugs has been urged recently by R T Trevillion.[2] I should emphasize, however, that in Britain choices about refining the techniques for evaluating drugs rest mainly, at present, with the pharmaceutical companies and with the medical profession. The procedures for licensing drugs require demonstration only of safety and efficacy – not a full cost-effectiveness analysis. The Pharmaceutical Price Regulation Scheme influences the price of drugs indirectly, via regulation of profits, but does not necessitate the sort of detailed negotiations over the prices of individual drugs which occurs in some countries and which might necessitate demonstration of cost-effectiveness. Nevertheless, at least from the stand-point of the British tax payer, who finances the NHS, the more that doctors know about the potential health yield and cost of drugs the better (other things being equal). The results of more comprehensive evaluation could be disseminated to the medical profession by well established routes such as the main medical journals, *Drug and Therapeutics Bulletin*, the *Prescribers Journal*, and the *British National Formulary*.

Caution

At this point you may well feel that my enthusiasm has gone quite far enough, so I will turn to the cautious side of my attitude to the new measures.

The acid test for health status measures is whether, via their contribution to the quality of clinical and NHS decision making, they can improve the allocation of resources sufficiently to outweigh the costs entailed in their preparation. There are certain causes for hesitation about this.

Measurement versus Judgement

One possible view of formal evaluation in general and health status measurement in particular is that it is unnecessary. Why should not drug and other therapies be tested by clinical trial and error? Will not the best judgements be made by the general body of clinicians who, in the normal course of their work, get to know their patients and can observe closely the effect of their treatments upon them?

Such an approach has been given a limited (post-marketing) role so far as drug safety is concerned. Moreover, since publication of *Effectiveness and Efficiency* by A L Cochrane we have become more aware of the many examples of inefficiency, and abandoned therapies that sprinkle the history of medicine and more inclined to argue with Cochrane that, '. . . the problem of evaluation is the first priority of the NHS'.[3] More recently, reports both in the US (Office of Technology Assessment, 1982) and in the UK (Council for Science and Society, 1982) have concluded that many new medical techniques are given inadequate evaluation.[4,5] The latter report concluded specifically that

'The criteria applied in the evaluation of (Expensive Medical Techniques)

have tended to be narrow, being restricted to such things as mortality, morbidity or medical assessments of function. These last may differ from patients' views of what the impact on themselves has been. The experience of patients and their relatives should be evaluated systematically in the course of randomised control trials. The best way to do this is for observers independent of those directly involved in the development of the (Expensive Medical Technique) to gather information systematically at suitable times from the patients themselves and their relatives.'

Validity of health status measures

Although there may be support for the idea that better measures of outcome are needed in medical evaluation it seems that there is not yet a consensus on how to achieve them. The use of mortality as a measure of outcome is well established but there seem to be several schools of thought on how to measure morbidity or quality of life. Earlier papers in this volume have described examples of two major approaches – health profiles and global indices. Only the latter provide clear guidance for resource allocation decisions. The Nottingham Health Profile is based currently on six separate dimensions of health (physical mobility, pain, sleep, energy, social isolation and emotional reactions) and eschews weighting of these different dimensions. The Rosser/Kind 'scale', as we have seen, is based currently on only two dimensions of health – disability and distress – and weights each dimension to produce a global index. It can be argued that health profiles are only the penultimate step on the way to the construction of global indices or, to put it another way, that global indices can always be disaggregated into health profiles. Nevertheless, some people feel instant scepticism when confronted with global indices because they require individuals to place precise numerical values on the widely disparate dimensions of health (or its lack) including death. It is perfectly clear that, by their behaviour, individuals, doctors and health administrators arrive at *implicit* trade-offs between different health states (see, for example, Hurst and Mooney; reference 6). It is equally clear that they do not find it very easy to articulate these trade-offs *explicitly*.

Whose values?

The Rosser/Kind work quoted in this paper, suggests not only that there are wide differences between individuals in health scales but also that there are (consistent?) differences in scales between groups such as doctors, nurses, sick patients and healthy volunteers. This is not surprising, perhaps, but it does raise questions about whose values are to count in measuring health status. The economists' snap answer would be, 'the consumer' but since experience of ill health seems to affect.values a more considered reply might be, 'the experienced consumer'. Of course, sickness may affect judgement. To the extent that it is feasible, the right approach might be to try to coax patients to recall the unpleasant feelings and experiences associated with sickness (and treatment) after recovery. Of course, most ex-patients have experienced only a selection of health states.

The time dimension in health status measurement

Health states are treated either as permanent or of indefinite duration in the Rosser/Kind index, employed above. This limits somewhat the applicability of this index since most treatments have the characteristics of an investment – that is they produce durable but finite changes in health status – and, unfortunately, the only permanent state on offer to man is death. What we require, surely, are values for health states (apart from death) which last for a given period such as one year, together with measures of the rate at which individuals discount the future. The discount rate may vary widely between individuals, judging by the different attitudes to prevention found in society. Assuming that all individuals should be treated equally, we would then have a longitudinal unit of account for health status and a method of aggregating such units. The Quality Adjusted Life Year (QALY) devised by Weinstein and Stason seems to be a useful example of a longitudinal unit of account.[7]

Attitudes to risk and uncertainty

At any one moment, the future course of health and the efficacy of most treatments are uncertain for the individual although they are much more predictable for a population. Attitudes to risk vary between individuals. Barbara McNeil *et al* have shown that some patients, offered a choice between radiotherapy and surgical treatment for lung cancer, preferred the former despite the lower five-year survival rate under radiotherapy.[8] This is because surgery carries greater immediate risks of death and many individuals prefer better prospects of immediate survival to better prospects of distant survival. McNeil *et al* argue that, 'These results emphasise the importance of choosing therapies not only on the basis of objective measures of survival but also on the basis of patient attitudes'.

The cost of measuring health status

What will it cost to add health status measurement to clinical trials and evaluation? Clearly health status measurement adds to the complexity of evaluations and, to the extent that it goes hand in hand with asking wider questions about alternative treatments, it also tends to extend the scope of evaluation. Additional evaluation of drugs may delay the time at which effective preparations can be brought to market, with consequent loss of benefits to consumers and disincentives for future investment in pharmaceutical research by the pharmaceutical companies. Clearly, any extensions to evaluation techniques should themselves be submitted to the discipline of cost-effectiveness scrutiny.

Who would finance and organise the use of health status measurement in evaluation?

Even if it could be shown (by trial and error, or by launching demonstration projects), that a more determined approach to measuring health status would easily recoup its costs, by supplying valid information, which led to an improved allocation of health service resources, questions would remain about how extra evaluation of drugs and other treatments should be organised and financed.

Would the pharmaceutical industry see it as in its interests to undertake health status measurement in evaluation? Would the government, on behalf of the users of drugs and the taxpayer, seek to introduce regulations to require manufacturers to mount fuller evaluation? Or would the NHS organise and finance independent evaluation using the new measures? I leave these questions to be answered, as occasion arises, by others.

Conclusion

The introduction of valid and reliable health status measurement into clinical evaluation in general, and drug evaluation in particular, would transform the debate about resource allocation in health services. Improving health status is a common goal for health service activities yet, without a way of measuring this yield, the value of activities cannot be compared formally and the search for efficiency is hampered by ambiguity. In recent years there has been an upsurge of activity by various research groups in devising new comprehensive measures of health status. However, a variety of questions can be raised about the likely acceptability, efficacy and cost of applying these measures and about who would organise and finance their use. On the whole, the papers in this volume suggest that the answers to these questions may not lie far ahead. Those charged with the evaluation of health services and therapies are showing growing interest in measures of outcome. Some are using simple or partial measures of the health yield from therapy. Others, as the papers in this volume by Martin Buxton and Morton Paterson suggest, are now using the new comprehensive measures of health status. Perhaps the research phase in health status measurement is drawing to a close and the development phase has begun.

REFERENCES

1 Rosser R and Kind P, 'A Scale of Valuations of States of Illness: is there a Social consensus?' *International Journal of Epidemiology*, Vol 7 No 4, 1978.
2 Trevillion R T, *The Rational Evaluation of Drug Therapies: The Role of Economics;* Discussion Paper No 05/81, Health Economics Research Unit, University of Aberdeen, 1981.
3 Cochrane A L, *Effectiveness and Efficiency.* Nuffield Provincial Hospitals Trust, 1972.
4 Office of Technology Assessment. *Strategies for Medical Technology Assessment,* Congress of the United States, Washington DC, September 1982.
5 Council for Science and Society. *Expensive Medical Techniques:* Report of a Working Party, 1982.
6 Hurst J W and Money G. 'Implicit values in Administrative Decisions' in A J Culyer (Ed.) *Health Indicators,* St Martins Press, New York, 1983.
7 Weinstein M C and Stason W B. *Hypertension: A Policy Perspective,* Harvard UP, 1976.
8 McNeil B J, Weichselbaum R and Pauker S G. 'Fallacy of the five year survival in lung cancer' *New England Journal of Medicine.* Vol 299 No 25, 21 December 1978.

Sociopharmacology and social benefits. The relevance of judgement analysis to drug development

C. R. B. Joyce
CIBA-GEIGY; Basel

What is sociopharmacology?

It is not clear who first used the term sociopharmacology to describe, by analogy with psychopharmacology, the use of the methods of social psychology to elucidate the action of drugs, and the use of drugs to illuminate the variables of social functioning. Although work that would today be described by that term was in progress much earlier, Lennard was apparently the first to use it in print.[1] By now it is commonly accepted.[2] Most work in the field seems, so far, to have been more concerned with the influence of social factors upon drug response than with that of drugs upon social behaviour. One rather special aspect of the latter will be emphasized here: the relationship between drug development and the social processes involved in decision-making, especially the perception of drug-related risk. All stages in drug development – the industrial, the regulatory and the clinical – involve this kind of judgement.

Judgemental tasks in drug development

The task of the regulator resembles that of the manager as well as that of the scientist and physician, who have to collect the facts upon which judgement will be based. Managers and regulators have to evaluate facts within the context of their company or country's policies, taking into account, in addition, estimates of political, social and economic factors that are hardly likely to be as factual as those from the laboratory. On the other hand, the clinician's intellectual behaviour is somewhere between those which are typical of the laboratory and the boardroom. It is no mere coincidence that he (or she) speaks of the 'management' of the patient. The physician's tasks are to arrive at a diagnosis on the basis of tests and clinical observations, to select the most appropriate treatment on the basis of his evaluation of available knowledge and to predict the outcome from these facts and evaluations. To do this, he will elicit a history from the patient, many items of which consist of exact measurements (age, duration of illness, certain fairly precise signs, etc) but others of which are less direct (severity of symptoms, level of mood, intelligence, etc.)

From an over-simple point of view, all human activity consists of measurement, followed by judgement, sometimes also followed by action. Frequently, measurement is not explicit and much of the time it is even unconscious; the system of homeostatic controls operated by the autonomic nervous system is of this kind. Even many of our conscious measurements are little more than running estimations, and the judgements, or comparisons, that we base upon these (as, for example, whether to cross the road now or wait until three more cars have passed, or whether or not to continue reading this paper in the hope that it will eventually say something interesting) are handled at an almost reflex level – although on occasions they might benefit from more conscious attention than they normally get. Even in the much more complex social field, where behaviour involves cooperation or antagonism between two or more individuals, or other kinds of relationship – are there any other kinds? – these mechanisms are still at work. It would be possible to illustrate this thesis from any walk of life, including the provision of health care.

Scientists, including doctors, as well as regulators and managers are all at times inclined to make statements supported less by facts than by conviction, especially if the topic is not one in which they have a professional interest or of which they possess first-hand knowledge. If they do, their statements are more likely to be distinguished by caution, moderation and sometimes accuracy. However, they have not only to make statements but also to take decisions, and here, too, facts and opinions must usually be fused together for action. This is true even if, as sometimes seems better, it is desired to follow a course of positive inaction, rather than of slavery to activity for its own sake.

It is not possible to escape from the tyranny by refusing to make a judgement or to take a decision. To do nothing is a decision to maintain the *status quo*. Inaction or continuation of an action without change does not obliterate risk; it selects one set of risks from the population of all risks. For example, Shapiro *et al* have shown that the indirect as well as direct costs of vaginal and abdominal hysterectomy may be reduced, without sacrificing the benefits, by *omitting* prophylaxis with antibiotics, especially if these are expensive.[3]

Steps involved in judgement

Decisions to act or not to act must be made by applying values to whatever facts there are. Some facts are usually available, even if these only emphasize the extent of ignorance, or consist of simple lists of facilities, locations of people, etc, to whom the decisions will have to be applied. Judgement first requires the establishment of such facts as there are, or their replacement or amplification by guesses or other expressions of opinion before this information can be combined into a judgement at all. The two functions, of acquiring the basic data and combining them in judgements should be kept separate. Problems arise when decision-makers usurp the role of fact-finders, or when the latter are forced to make the decisions because those whose proper task this is fail to discharge it.[4]

Laboratory science is seldom carried out in absolute independence of philosophical and, especially these days, economic or political pressures, but it does possess rules for the collection and evaluation of data and rejection of hypotheses. Social experiments seldom resemble those in laboratories; facts are usually harder to come by and to retain, opinions easier to formulate and express.

Facts are sometimes classified as 'hard' (instrumentally derived) or 'soft' (intelligence tests, etc); opinions are always considered to be soft. The distinction between hard and soft is notoriously difficult to sustain, especially in medicine. The blood pressure may be recorded in millimetres of mercury, but its level is influenced by the mood of the patient as well as the accuracy of the observer's perception; the red blood cell count is given as an exact number, but it is estimated from a sample judged to be representative. Laboratory examinations indeed provide measures that are usually easier to quantify than those from clinical observation or the opinions expressed by the patient, but the point is not whether the information can be quantified but whether it can be exteriorized. If it is exteriorizable, and reliably so, it can be scientifically studied. It is a frequent misconception that if the data are 'objective', decisions can be made without 'subjective' judgements. The occasions on which only hard data need to be considered in making a judgement are so rare that it is difficult to think of a single example, whether from management, regulation or clinical medicine.

The manufacturer, for example, only begins work after a judgement that the molecule he is attempting to synthesize, or to extract from a biological starting-point, will show measurable, useful activity. His chemist may synthesize a series of a hundred or a thousand components, the probable value of which will be evaluated in model systems of progressively increasing complexity. Meanwhile, still far away from being introduced into a human being for the first time, and further still from commercialization, the possible toxicity must also be studied, the predicted risks and benefits of use compared. Later, clinical comparisons with other compounds used in the relevant indications will be made. The costs of scaled-up production, market chances, the time required before the compound begins to pay back its costs of development, and that which remains for it to contribute to profits before the patent expires must be predicted. The newer, or especially the more original, the drug, the less likely it is that 'facts' will be available to help the judgements that must be made about its future.

The consequences of the judgements of the regulators, as of the managers, for the health of the company as well as of society at large, are often international, although the viewpoint of an individual regulatory authority is usually national, or at most regional. For example, an extremely useful and inexpensive antihypertensive, widely used throughout the world, was suspected by one important authority on the basis of preliminary epidemiological study to be carcinogenic. Although such a judgement was subsequently shown to be almost certainly unjustified, the drug had already to a large extent been replaced by more expensive remedies that developing countries could less easily afford.

To treat his patient, the physician selects and combines items of information about alternative diagnoses, risk factors and other epidemiological variables, and advantages of potential alternatives for treatment. Much of this information, including that about the patient he is treating, will already have been stored in his memory, and only rarely will he need to go to his textbooks, journals, that morning's waste paper basket or – perhaps more often in the future – to his computer terminal to seek for more, relevant information. Even if he has only to give an injection, measurements, comparisons and judgements will still be needed. Judging where to insert the needle, an apparently trivial operation in itself, involves the comparison of current perceptions with previous experience, to a large extent subconsciously.

Public criticism of expert judgement

There is one further important resemblance between the manufacturer, the regulator and the physician: the volume of criticism directed at their actions, some of it from their own professional colleagues, is steadily increasing. This may be desirable, but it is also in part due to the application of different judgements to similar sets of facts. In commenting upon a recent Reith lecturer's suggestion that the exercise of medical expertise, especially in psychiatry, is really that 'of moral, social and political judgement concerning the worth of someone's thinking,' and that this awful power ought to be devolved to lay people,[5] the British Medical Journal made the good point that 'if it is morally wrong for doctors to control patients it may not be any more right for patients to control doctors;'[6] or, one may add, for other groups to control both of them. It is clearly necessary not only to decide how the quality of decisions in general could be improved, but also who should achieve this. Lay and expert estimates of risk often differ.[7] The public perception of risk rises in parallel to the extent to which that risk is involuntarily embraced, rather than to the actual frequency with which the risk leads to death or damage.[8] Rockclimbing, rugby, driving and smoking are much more often attended by accident than flying, medication or exposure to nuclear radiation, yet are voluntarily practised. The latter, on the other hand, all require, to a greater or lesser extent, that the individual surrender control over his fate to someone else, who becomes heavily regulated instead.

The increase in volume of criticism is perhaps a reflection of unease about the performance of specialist functions in society as a whole. The automobile industry, alcohol and tobacco manufacturers and others, and their regulatory organizations, are increasingly coming in for criticism as well.

The perception of risk

The American medical sociologist Irving Zola some years ago coined a phrase that is now on many people's lips: 'Living is dangerous to your health'. This was always an understatement: living is not merely dangerous, but lethal. Being born is guaranteed to bring life to an end, though the decision is not made by the individual himself, but usually by two others who may not exercise much prior judgement either. Although the degree of voluntariness or compulsion is not the only factor to determine risk, 19 of the 32 'aspects of risk' listed by Vlek and Stallen are considered by the authors to be associated with the voluntariness or controllability of exposure, the severity and nature of the consequences, and contextual variables related to these.[9] There is good evidence that information about the extent to which accidents have occurred in the past does not lead to more accurate prediction of risk. High-frequency events, such as death by cancer, tend to be underestimated, while low-frequency untoward events, such as those due to drugs, are over-estimated. This is not *only* because rare events are news although this may well be a contributory factor. Many other influences upon judgement have been documented.[10,11] A dramatic recent event tends to dominate a contrary earlier one, a single personal experience the much larger number in a scientific survey. Pressures – of time, or to come to a definite conclusion – or the statistical, semantic or syllogistic way in which the question is put can be enormously influential.[12, 13]

Even when facts are unavailable, in short supply, or inaccurate, judgements are still made, if only implicitly; but judgements that remain implicit are more likely to lead to subsequent misunderstandings, whether or not they were originally correct. Minutes of the proceedings of committees are often considered to be unsatisfactory, even by those who participated in the discussions that gave rise to them, very largely because they concentrate upon end-product rather than process. The less the extent to which a decision is reached is retraceable at any time after the event, the more likely is the decision itself to be disputed. If data are missing, opinions vehement and judgement confident, yet divisive and changeable (especially if there is no awareness that this is so), more science is needed, not less. Such techniques of so-called management science as Delphi prediction are as mystical and anti-scientific as any other kind of fortune-telling, and do not excuse failure to develop scientific methods for handling intractable problems.

La Rochefoucauld might have been writing today instead of 300 years ago when he noted that 'Everybody complains of his memory, but nobody of his judgement'.[14] Computers are now widely used to expand individual and group memory, and to give it a reliable base. With their aid, judgements can be explicitly described in such a way that they can be made self-consistent and so become more likely to reflect the actual intentions of their authors. They can then be discussed with others in a constructive fashion that is impossible if they remain implicit. To do this efficiently, the possible outcomes of alternative courses of action need first to be distinguished carefully and exhaustively. This is possible even in medicine as has been repeatedly shown, for example by Pauker,[15] in regard to coronary artery surgery, and Hogarth[11] discussing the monitoring of adverse reactions to drugs, Fisch et al in psychiatry and Kirwan et al in rheumatology.[16,17] This is all the more necessary, in so far as it is likely that two or more judges will be concerned and two observers of a common set of data will make quite a different use of the same cues and so will disagree in their judgements. It is sometimes objected that such diversity is good, the very stuff of which good decisions are made. But it can be shown that, despite his self-confidence, a judge can seldom fully represent even to himself what information (the 'cues') he is using in arriving at a judgement and the way in which he differentially weights these cues and combines them to form the judgement. Even if, exceptionally, he is fully aware of the cues, he will almost certainly use them inconsistently, giving small weight to one factor on one occasion and more on another, even when the two situations are identical. The form of the relation of cue and judgement, as well as the way in which information may be transformed before or during combination of cues may also change and so lower the reliability of the judge's behaviour.

Who should judge?
As patients, as well as in our other roles, we would all like totally safe drugs, but these do not exist. We should like also drugs of guaranteed effectiveness for each individual, but these do not exist either. Yet a curious im-

balance in the perception of safety and efficacy seems to have grown up with the years; whereas the report of a serious, even if extremely rare, unwanted effect may cause an effective drug to be withdrawn from the market before the report has been substantiated, evidence of real benefit to a small, but important, number of patients is unlikely to secure its admission to the market even in the absence of toxicity. Where does the responsibility lie, not for designing and executing clinical trials to the highest standards (which is clearly that of the manufacturer, the investigator and the regulatory authority together), but for ensuring that the information derived from them is used with maximal efficiency? This also involves an important moral question, for an inefficient trial is immoral.[18] This responsibility is at present not clearly defined or correctly distributed.

In the last analysis we are all, producers as well as prescribers, patients. There are few if any products in the world apart from medicines of which it is so sure that each of us will one day need them. This realization should give a unique perspective to the exercise of judgement by producers and consumers about the use of medicines.

The improvement of judgement
First of all, the possible outcomes of a given trial should as far as possible be judged by the investigators a well as other interested parties in advance. Decisions about Type 1 and Type 2 error levels, stopping rules, the definition of countable events,[19] as well as interpretations of outcome and recommendations for actions based upon these should be arrived at systematically, explicitly and in advance. The judgements of regulatory authorities are also applied to the outcome of clinical trials. The efficacy and toxicity of these should be studied as intensively as the investigations that are their subject-matter;[20] as should the impact of the media, which is not unrelievedly beneficial. All these judgements should be openly arrived at and evaluated.

How to decide whom to consult (ie, whose judgements are relevant) is itself a problem that needs to be attacked with the methods of judgement analysis. If consumers are to be consulted, producers should be, too. Physicians, where drugs are concerned, should be considered as both. The purpose is to reach agreement, or at least to have the reasons for disagreement clearly recorded. First, there must clearly be adequate discussion of controversial topics. Every possibly relevant factor should be brought fully into the open so that the judges can be helped to evaluate its importance, in terms of their own conceptual framework. Comparing and combining strands of evidence into a judgement are not activities that the human analogue computer carries out reliably,[21] whereas such activities can be performed rapidly, accurately and with complete consistency by computers furnished with appropriate programmes. The case is therefore strong for establishing symbiosis between the two. The human judge must be helped, by the provision of a sufficient number of test cases, to formulate his policy; after it has become visible in this way, the policy can be modified by the individual or by a relevant group. After an agreed policy has been arrived at, however, it should be applied with absolute consistency. Several procedures are suitable for the purpose.[22] Although the method that we have used is based on sophisticated multiple regression analysis[23] it appears from many experimental results that real-life human judgement can often be satisfactorily simulated by a rather simple linear model.

Further illustrations

There are other situations in which the systematic use of computer-assisted judgement could play a role in improving the kinds of inference about outcomes to which reference has been made.

First, when considering the social implications of drug-induced disorders, those whose suffering is clearly due to the treatment should be identified and, in accordance with applicable law, adequately compensated. This is good epidemiology and good morals. It requires that the disease be first defined and differentiated from others that it resembles, and that what constitutes adequate evidence that the drug has been taken also be decided.[24] Not all drug-induced disorders are as clear-cut as that induced by thalidomide. The solution of the problems that arise would benefit, or might have benefited, from the application of judgement analysis by the parties concerned. Second, in relation to many problems evidence is often accumulated about a suspected relationship between exposure to a drug and an increased incidence of certain symptoms from a number of studies, epidemiological and toxicological. Can observations from studies widely differing in their intent, methodology and results be combined to give a useful overall assessment? To put the question in an extreme form, can data on 8,078 patients be added to that from 984 rodents in a valid way?[25] The answer is: 'yes', although this is seldom if ever done.

Third, editors are notoriously unwilling to publish information from studies giving negative results, although this leads to distortion and delay in the search for truth. Such information could perhaps be combined without the need for detailed publication in each case.

Last, although it may not be unreasonable that two or more national regulatory authorities reach opposite conclusions on the basis of the same evidence,[26] the relevant questions are seldom put in a way that allows the reasons for different responses to be understood and the responses themselves to be synthesized.

'Judgements in cause-effect reasoning have troubled medical scientists throughout the centuries', says Feinstein, pointing out that for many (essentially judgemental) questions 'we not only lack satisfactory answers, we do not even generally agree that the current methods of research are suitable, in both scientific logic and practical feasibility, for getting the answers'.[20] Many examples considered here bear upon the question of causality: does this drug or disease cause, or is it likely to cause, this effect? This kind of problem is often typified by a mixture of analytical and intuitive, so-called 'quasi-rational', thinking. Methodology for the scientific use of both kinds of thinking, especially for their combination, is available.[22,23]

REFERENCES

1 Lennard H L: A Proposed Program of Research in Sociopharmacology. In: Psychobiological Approaches to Social Behaviour. Leiderman P H and Shapiro D (eds.). London: Tavistock, pp, 127 –137, 1965.

2 McGuire M T: Sociopharmacology. Ann Rev Pharmacol Toxicol, 22, 643–661, 1982.

3 Shapiro M, Schoenbaum S C, Tager I B, Munoz A, Polk B F: Benefit-cost Anlysis of Anti-microbial Prophylaxis in Abdominal and Vaginal Hysterectomy. *J Amer Med Ass, 249,* 1290–1294, 1983.

4 Crawford D A: Fagan – a Suitable Case for Treatment. *Bull Brit Psychol Soc, 36,* 153–155, 1983.

5 Swales J D: Thoughts on the Reith Lectures. *Lancet, 2,* 1348–50, 1980.

6 Editorial: The Reith Lectures: Style, Responsibility, and Accountability. *Brit Med J, 281,* 1659–60, 1980.

7 Slovic P, Fischhoff B, Lichtenstein S: Facts and Fears: Understanding Perceived Risk. In : Schwing R C, Albers W A, Jr, (eds.): Societal Risk Assessment: How Safe is Safe Enough? New York: Plenum Press, 1980.

8 Kletz T A: Benefits and Risks: Their Assessment in Relation to Human Needs. *Endeavour, 4,* 46–51, 1980.

9 Vlek C, Stallen P J: Rational and Personal Aspects of Risk. *Acta Psychol, 45,* 273–300, 1980.

10 Hammond K R and Joyce C R B: Psychological Influences on Human Judgment, Especially of Adverse Reactions. In: Drug Monitoring. Gross F H, Inman W H W (eds.) pp 269–278. London: Academic Press, 1977.

11 Hogarth R M: Judgment and Choice. Chichester: John Wiley and Sons, 1980.

12 Fischhoff B, Slovic P, Lichtenstein S: Lay Foibles and Expert Fables in Judgments about Risk. In: O'Riordan T, Turner R K (eds.): Progress in Resource Management and Environmental Planning, Vol 3, Chichester: Wiley, 1980.

13 Kahneman D, Tversky A: On the Pyschology of Prediction. *Psychol Rev, 80,* 237–251, 1973.

14 La Rochefoucauld: Maximes, 1678. Trans. Tancock L W. Harmondsworth: Penguin, 1959.

15 Pauker S G: Coronary Artery Surgery – the Use of Decision Analysis. *Ann Int Med, 85,* 8–18, 1976.

16 Fisch H U, Hammond K R, Joyce C R B, O'Reilly M: An Experimental Study of the Clinical Judgment of General Physicians in Evaluating and Prescribing for Depression. *Brit J Psychiat, 138,* 100–109, 1981.

17 Kirwan J R, Chaput de Saintonge D M, Joyce C R B, Currey H L F: Clinical Judgment Analysis – Practical Application in Rheumatology. *Brit J Rheumatol,* in press, 1983.

18 Sackett D L: Hard Data, Soft Data, Defects in Design and Advice for the Future. In: Platelets, Drugs and Thromboses. Hirsch J, Cade J F, Gallus A S, Schönbaum E (eds.). Basel: Karger, 1975.

19 Sackett D L, Gent M: Controversy in Counting and Attributing Events in Clinical Trials. *New Engl J Med, 301,* 1410–1412, 1979.

20 Feinstein A R: The Patient, the Physician, and the Regulator. *Forum Med, 2,* 652–656, 1979.

21 Einhorn H J: Expert Measurement and Mechanical Combination. *Organizat Beh Perform, 7,* 86–106, 1972.

22 Hammond K R, McClelland G H and Mumpower J: Human Judgment and Decision Making. Theories, Methods and Procedures. New York: Praeger, 1980.

23 Hammond K R and Joyce C R B: Psychoactive Drugs and Social Judgment. New York: Wiley Interscience, 1975.

24 Meade T W: Sub-acute Myelo-Optic Neuropathy and Clioquinol: An Epidemiological Case-History for Diagnosis. *Brit J Prev Soc Med, 29,* 157–169, 1975.

25 Clemmesen J, Hjalgrim-Jensen S: A Follow-up for Cancer through 1943–1972 among 8078 Epileptics admitted for Anticonvulsant Therapy 1933–1962. Proc First Internat Cong Toxicol, pp 269–283. New York Academic Press, 1978.

26 Wardell W M and Lasagna L: Regulation and Drug Development. Washington DC: American Enterprise Institute for Public Policy Research, 1975.

L

Medicines evaluation: the future

David Taylor
Office of Health Economics

The papers in this volume are largely concerned to describe the attempts of health economists and clinicians to evaluate the social benefits of medicines and other health care interventions. The two main objectives of this last contribution relate to a somewhat different goal. First, it attempts to position this type of investigative work within the wider context of health services research (HSR). The boundaries of this broad domain of intellectual enquiry are indicated in Table 1. Second, it examines how pharmaceutical companies might participate more in HSR in general and the evaluation of the social benefits and costs of medicines in particular, so more effectively to pursue their legitimate interests.

The approach adopted involves the presentation of an initial overview of HSR development in this country; then a look at the relationships between the various disciplines working in the field; and finally an analysis of the potential advantages of pharmaceutical industry social research initiatives and a brief discussion of the options currently open for stimulating the latter. Although most of the detailed comment made in the paper applies specifically to English experience in this area, the ideas put forward are relevant to many of the problems faced by medicine consumers, prescribers and producers right across Western Europe and North America.

The history of health services research in England

Table 2 lists some of the key dates relating to the evolution of HSR in twentieth century Britain, a pattern of gradual progress which itself rests on the pioneer work of nineteenth century investigators and evaluators like William Farr – the first Registrar General – and Florence Nightingale.

In 1911 the passing of the National Insurance Act brought with it not only a new system of financing primary care for working people, but also the formation of the forerunner of today's Medical Research Council (MRC). It was known as the Medical Research Committee, and had a special remit to look at the social as well as the biomedical aspects of tuberculosis.

In 1919 an Act which established both the Ministry of Health and the MRC in near to its current form was passed. These two bodies worked in a manner largely separate from one another in the interwar years. The Ministry was concerned with public health policies and addressed itself primarily to the health authorities, the body politic and the community as a

TABLE 1   **The purposes of health services research (HSR)**

To provide descriptive information in the health sphere.

To develop and to test specific hypotheses.

To evaluate actual or potential health care outcomes.

To aid and or analyse health policy formation.

TABLE 2   **HSR in the UK: key dates**

	1911	National Insurance Act Medical Research Committee formed.
	1919	Ministry of Health and MRC established.
	1948	NHS – new factors emerge.
	1960	MOH/DHSS develop research in services: a 'golden age'?
Phase 1	1965	SSRC formed.
	1971	Rothschild customer/contractor principle urged.
Phase 2	1981	The 'Buller' crisis in HSR, cuts threaten SSRC and UGC research. MRC regains transferred funds.
Phase 3?	1983	New stability? Joint MRC/SSRC/DHSS projects planned.

whole; the MRC's natural audience was the specialised medical research cadre, whose interests focused at the individual or cellular level rather than the collective one.

However, the formation of the NHS in 1948 went hand in hand with the appearance of new conditions and factors destined in some respects to challenge the discrete roles of the MoH and the MRC. These included the control of acute infectious diseases as major health problems in Britain, and the gradual emergence of chronic degenerative disorders like senility and arthritis as the most significant causes of morbidity. This shift has required the health service to become involved in elaborate and costly forms of medical and social support, and thus complicated its functional characteristics and information needs. This in itself stimulated demands for the types of HSR activity outlined in Table 1.

Also the advent of more sophisticated medical techniques and technologies has proved to be another element behind increasing NHS costs and managerial difficulties. In the early 1960s the MoH (or Department of Health and Social Security as it became in 1968) began to invest in evaluative research activity in its own right. Amongst the first problems investigated were the potential costs and benefits of mass screening programmes then being proposed.

In retrospect a number of health services researchers have come to see 1960–1970 as a 'golden age' of relatively free innovative activity on the part of the research community supported by the Ministry. But by the end of the decade, as Table 2 indicates, this gave way to a new, less satisfactory, phase. This followed the publication and government acceptance of the Rothschild report on state research activities, which firmly advocated a more disciplined customer/contractor relationship. In short, those Departments paying for research were urged to lay down precise details of the work they wanted done, not to leave it to the researchers themselves to identify the issues they judged as in most need of investigation.

In fact it would be wrong to suggest that the Rothschild report alone was responsible for the events of the 1970s. British science management was already in a state of some flux, a fact indicated by events like the dissolution of the old Department of Scientific and Industrial Research and the establishment of the Science, Social Science and Natural Environmental Research Councils in the mid 1960s. But there is no doubt that the post Rothschild transfer of a quarter of the MRC's funds to the DHSS in 1972/73 (intended to facilitate DHSS purchases of MRC studies) became a major source of tension between the two bodies.

Also the DHSS's efforts to manage its own research programme more precisely via the Chief Scientists Office set up in that year were fraught with many problems. It proved extremely difficult for civil servants in practice to play the role of informed research customers.

The 'second phase' of HSR development reached a crisis point at the start of the 1980s. At least three sets of reasons helped to account for this. First, a number of senior individuals in the area, including heads of DHSS financed units, found the critical approach of the then Chief Scientist, Professor Arthur Buller, uncongenial. Second, there were fears that financial restrictions would curtail not only DHSS HSR work but might also endanger the Social Science Research Council and the entire dual University Grants Council/Research Councils research funding system. Third, 1981 saw the return of the transferred funds to the MRC (where Professor Buller had previously been a Board Chairman) in exchange for a pledge that the Council would become more closely involved in HSR.

This last would seem to have been a victory for those believing in the internalist view of science, that is that researchers should be in control of the direction and objectives of their own work. Yet some individuals in HSR believed that if the MRC took over control of the area the attitudes and interests of natural or biomedical scientists would prove alien or hostile to those of individuals like economists and sociologists. Despite assurances to the effect that the DHSS did not intend to 'hand-over' its HSR interests to the MRC such doubts fuelled an atmosphere of distrust and dismay.

However, this crisis now appears to have passed over. Support for bodies like the SSRC and the DHSS HSR units has been by and large maintained, albeit with certain financial cuts. Sir Desmond Pond has taken over the role of the Chief Scientist at the DHSS, together with Professor Robin Cole as his deputy. The relationship between researchers and the DHSS appears stronger. The MRC has begun to investigate the HSR possibilities open to it via an advisory Health Services Research Panel, but has certainly taken no precipitate action likely to threaten the interests of HSR investigators. Table 3 indicates the current levels of funding.

In conclusion to this very brief summary of the history of HSR in England it may be argued that its progress has now entered a third phase, in which

TABLE 3 **Main HSR funding agencies in the UK (1982)**

DHSS SHHD	c. £10 million
MRC	c. £2 million
SSRC	c.£0.5 million
Charities	£1–2 million?
UGC	<£0.5 million?
Industry	?
Total	<£15 million
UK Biomedical and clinical R & D = c. £500 million	

Source: OHE estimates.

hopefully there will be a more pragmatic balance between the 'internalist' and the 'customer/contractor' models of science management than has to date been achieved. As the work of Professor Kogan of Brunel University has shown, both approaches have virtues and drawbacks. A sensible compromise is needed, although one lesson of the last twenty or so years is that it will not easily be established.

Finally, it should also be noted that the total financial support available to the HSR community in the UK is unlikely to have exceeded £15 million in 1982. Nearly all this money comes from the state. This compares with the UK biomedical research budget of some £500 million in that year (of which some £300 million is contributed by the private pharmaceutical industry) and a total NHS budget of £15,000 million. In one sense the lack of evaluative and allied research suggested by these figures is disturbing, although they also show that if pharmaceutical companies choose to become more active HSR purchasers they would only have to spend limited sums in order to establish a substantial presence in the market-place.

The relationship between HSR disciplines

Figure 1 presents the entire area of health related research as a spectrum running from natural science investigations at one end through clinical medicine at the centre to health services research involving disciplines like sociology and economics at the other. There are two main points which can be made in relation to this simple model.

First, the type of phenomena being studied and the methods of observation and analysis employed differ significantly at different points on the spectrum. Towards the left the primary focus is at the systemic, cellular or even molecular level; 'hard' scientific techniques predominate. In the centre the clinician's main focus is on the individual, and his or her personal response to treatments. Whilst in HSR collective, social events are the main subject of attention; data are often available only in highly aggregated

FIGURE 1 **The Health Research Spectrum**

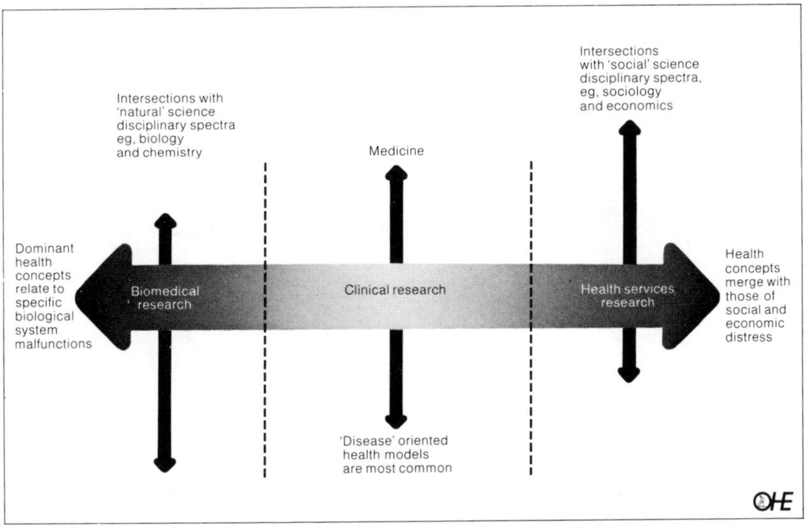

Intersections with 'social' science disciplinary spectra, eg, sociology and economics

Intersections with 'natural' science disciplinary spectra eg, biology and chemistry

Medicine

Dominant health concepts relate to specific biological system malfunctions

Biomedical research

Clinical research

Health services research

Health concepts merge with those of social and economic distress

'Disease' oriented health models are most common

OHE

form and may not always be open to validation via reproduction, at least in as much as unique social events cannot be precisely recreated.

Inevitable variations in disciplinary outlooks may sometimes be reflected in conflicts between individuals operating at different points in the spectrum shown. These may be aggravated by clashes over authority, particularly between medically qualified individuals (who usually regulate access to items like patient records and have a substantial control over resource allocations) and social scientists who fear domination by better established groups. Such factors may well have impeded HSR development.

Figure 2 concentrates attention on the linkages between certain HSR disciplines[1] Psychology is more like the natural sciences than are sociology or economics, although it is increasingly becoming seen as an essential 'feed' to both of the latter. The psychometric skills needed to create and operate the health status indices and profiles discussed in this volume illustrate this point. It is perhaps for this reason that psychologists now appear to have established an accepted position in both the health service and the research community and to have produced some work of unquestionable value – Mittler's extended programme of research on mental handicap is an outstanding example.

The position of medical sociology is somewhat more complex. Its origins as a sub-speciality in the UK date back to the early years of the NHS, when individuals with an interest in social phenomena were employed by academic medical departments concerned with public health and epidemiology to collect data relevant to such areas. It was in this way, for instance, that the MRC's medical sociology unit in Aberdeen became established.

But in the late 1950s/early 1960s mainstream sociology began to grow significantly in this country. In part because of economic incentives Universities expanded sociology departments rapidly, and the discipline had no

FIGURE 2   **The Relationships between selected HSR Disciplines**

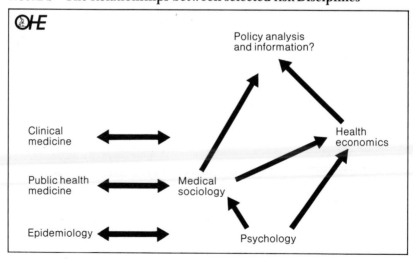

1   Disciplines like moral philosophy, demography and, perhaps most importantly, operational research, could also have been included here.

shortage of applicants from young people anxious to try to 'improve' society through, for instance, revealing the 'unacceptable' nature of the British class structure. It is fair to say that, for many, sociology was not a politically neutral science: rather it was a tool by which social(ist) ideals could be legitimated and achieved.

Neither this last trend nor the earlier circumstances which created posts in medical sociology stimulated good analytical work. The focus was much more on 'social arithmetic' and the untested assumption of simple causal relationships between factors like inequity and ill-health. Many people in government and industry became, and remain, sceptical of sociology in all its forms.

However, it should be emphasised that the sociology of health has considerable potential for contributing to any agency's work in the health care sector. Table 4 outlines the main areas it touches upon. Examples of activity in the fields noted can be drawn from the work of individuals like Brown, Macintyre, Stacey, Jefferys, Townsend, Strong, Illsley and Mechanic. Concepts generated within sociology such as those relating to, say, professionalisation, stigma or institutionalisation have proved to be of great significance in enhancing a humane understanding of health care problems. The 1980s 'third phase' of HSR development may well prove to be one in which sociology's contributions become more rationally accepted and acceptable.

Figure 2 suggests that health economics is to an extent dependent on medical sociology, in as much as the latter generates new insights into values and the social processes influencing human exchanges. Although some commentators appear to regard the models of man employed by economists as inherently discordant with those used by sociologists this is by no means necessarily the case, as Table 5 implies. Rather, if conflicts arise between exponents of the two disciplines it may be because economics, with its focus on the allocation of scarce resources, becomes frequently associated with attempts at demand limitation and rationing, whereas sociology, with its wider objective of elucidating social processes and interactions, may frequently serve to underline the existence of unmet – and perhaps unsuspected – 'need'.

Other questions raised by Figure 2 include that of whether or not there should be a separate discipline of policy analysis aimed at helping health sector decision makers to aggregate effectively all the advice coming from various sources and also several relating to the links between branches of the medical profession and the health services research community. This

TABLE 4   **Sociology's potential contributions to health care**

Revealing social factors which raise or lower health standards. Generating aetiological hypotheses.

Documenting beliefs relevant to health.

Documenting trends in overall behaviour relevant to health – demography, sexual habits, drinking etc.

Examining organisational dynamics of services.

Studying the development of policy.

TABLE 5 **Health Economics' contributions to health care**

Revealing the actual resource costs of services and items of care, so to provide measures of opportunities taken and foregone in alternative policies.

The identification of economically efficient choices (CEA, CBA).

The clarification of values implicit in particular patterns of resource allocation.

paper does not attempt to analyse either of these areas in detail. But two points are worthy of note.

First, it seems clear that at the political level economic and related analysis will never be regarded as offering definitive answers to policy questions. Although in Britain civil service interests and academic attitudes may have helped to slow the emergence of policy analysis as an independent specialism it may be that a more ordered and open approach to this area would have great value.

Second, one of the barriers to the development of HSR in the NHS at present may stem from the powerful position but seemingly disappointing performance of the specialists in community medicine, coupled with the fact that the NHS lacks adequate arrangements for employing researchers. It remains an open question as to whether or not the role and/or manning arrangements of community medicine departments may be changed for the better, one which might perhaps appropriately be investigated by a body such as the MRC, perhaps working in conjunction with SSRC and DHSS.

The advantages of pharmaceutical industry participation in HSR

There are two main ways in which increased pharmaceutical industry involvement in HSR generally and medicines evaluation specifically could generate advantages for the community. First, a greater plurality of purchasers would enhance the freedom of researchers in the field; the power of the state would be counterbalanced. It is worth noting that not all new medicines are likely to prove cost-saving as far as the NHS and the Treasury are concerned, even though they may vastly increase individual wellbeing amongst groups like the elderly. Sophisticated economic and sociological argument may be needed to justify the extended use of cost escalating

TABLE 6 **HSR's potential contribution to the pharmaceutical industry**

General. To describe and generate understanding of:

    a) consumer problems.
    b) media relations.
    c) political processes and policy formation.
    d) the overall value of existing and possible future pharmaceutical products to the community.

Specific. To identify for given products:

    a) a formal appreciation of their risks/benefits/costs and their potential and actual role in the community.
    b) to provide information relating to rational pricing.
    c) to help disseminate knowledge of the role and availability of established and new medicines.

pharmaceutical technologies, and of other types of care which may not provide direct, monetary, 'pay-offs' for the government.

Second, the pharmaceutical industry has much to gain from HSR – see Table 6. The possibility of innovation within industry designed to improve its contributions to the public good is obviously worthy of careful investigation.

Briefly, disciplined social and economic research programmes could help generate clearer understanding in fields ranging from media and consumer affairs on the one hand and third world health problems and state economic policies towards the pharmaceutical sector on the other. Focusing down to particular products, HSR may also help show how drug risks and benefits balance, and cast light on issues relating to prices and appropriate promotion. However, in this last context it must of course be emphasised that any lack of objectivity in pharmaceutical industry backed HSR would soon undermine its credibility.

It may also be noted that research on particular products is likely to be most worthwhile in cases where new modes of action and/or new therapeutic options are involved. Medicines like cimetidine and, currently, auranofin, captopril and the cyclosporins are obvious candidates for detailed analysis. Those which are representatives of a large group of alternative drugs may well warrant less specific attention. Studies aimed at elucidating broad treatment choices (for example, non-steroid anti-inflammatories for arthritis, with or without social support) or showing the pharmaceutical industry's overall need for a relatively high degree of market division (and hence inter-company income sharing) would seem most appropriate in these latter cases.

But desirable as pharmaceutical industry financed HSR might prove to be the previous sections of this paper indicate that the role of purchaser is by no means an easy one. For individual companies HSR customer/contractor problems may be amplified by a lack of the basic internal expertise needed even for efficient purchasing of research from external agencies, let alone for conducting studies 'in-house'. Methodological adequacy and appropriate costing are difficult to judge in the social studies field.

A powerful case can be made to the effect that in the medium to long term companies should make every effort to build up their own, permanent HSR capability. Only if disciplines like medical sociology and health economics come to exist securely within the managerial infrastructure of major firms are they likely to influence corporate attitudes and decisions to their full potential. Medical, marketing and public affairs departments are all potential workplaces for individuals with backgrounds in such areas, although public affairs may perhaps be thought most in need of both greater professionalisation and a more positive, consumer interest oriented role with the organisational structures of many large pharmaceutical enterprises.

Yet in the foreseeable future companies will remain very largely reliant on the service of specialist commercial bodies (such as, say, the Health Management Institute and Health Econ in Switzerland) and independent academic centres. In this context one possibility under consideration at OHE is that it should attempt to develop a capability designed to facilitate contracts between potential pharmaceutical industry purchasers of HSR and those individuals or groups who might be able to conduct competently the work needed.

Its envisaged brokerage role would involve insuring that on the one side industry may securely expect high quality, scientifically acceptable work delivered on-time and at a fair price; and that on the other researchers could be sure that acceptable use of their work would be made. To this end bodies like the MRC, the SSRC and the DHSS could be involved.

The data presented in this paper suggest that although there might be very substantial difficulties in establishing a health services research stimulating and coordinating body of the type indicated its contribution both to the pharmaceutical industry's future and the development of a more balanced network of HSR support in the UK could be substantial. Given the view of the recent Rothschild review of the SSRC that more industry/ Research Council cooperation is needed, and the fact that sums of £1 million or less could open up radically new areas of research progress, OHE will make every effort to explore the viability of this proposal.

FURTHER READING

OHE (1980) Health Research in England: a topic for debate. OHE. London.
Taylor D G and Teeling Smith G (In press). Health Services Research in England. (To be published by Longman as part of the UK Research Policy: A critical review. Ed M Goldsmith).
Kogan M and Henkel M (1983). Government and Research. The Rothschild Experiment. Heinemann Educational Books, London.

Issues for the future

George Teeling Smith
Office of Health Economics

During the discussion of the foregoing papers at Brunel, four questions arose. The first was whether it is desirable to introduce socio-economic methods of measurement to evaluate the outcome of new therapies, and new pharmaceutical preparations in particular. The second question was whether it was feasible to do so. Thirdly, the choice between 'health indicators' – giving a single scale of wellbeing – and 'health profiles' – giving a descriptive account of different aspects of wellbeing – was debated. Finally, the question arose as to when such measures should be introduced. This last question subdivided into two parts: first, how soon, if ever, could these measures of outcome start to be applied on a general basis; and, second, at what stage in the life of a new therapy should such evaluation be undertaken.

On the question of the general desirability of socio-economic measurements participants were fairly sharply divided. In my own introductory paper, I argued strongly that such measures have become necessary for two reasons. First, to provide a quantifiable 'benefit' side to the risk-benefit equation in relation to therapy. In recent months, the risks of medicines have dominated public discussion in the newspapers and on television, and the description of the benefit of medicines has been conspicuously lacking. Second, to justify the continually rising cost of all sectors of medical care. Any new therapy – whether it is a heart transplant or a new pharmaceutical – has to compete with alternative demands on scarce resources. It is certainly arguable that desirable patterns of therapeutic progress will be speeded up if their benefits are clearly demonstrated.

In the subsequent papers, and in the general discussion, the case for the use of socio-economic 'instruments' to measure wellbeing was supported by Martin Buxton, Jim McEwen, Mort Paterson, Rachel Rosser and Alan Williams. More tentatively, Jeremy Hurst also came out in favour of continuing to develop such instruments. On the other hand, Duncan Geddes, David Goldberg and Ted Huskisson – as practicing physicians – all expressed reservations over the value of any measures beyond the traditional clinical assessment of the benefits of therapy. In addition, members of the audience from the pharmaceutical industry expressed anxieties that the need to produce yet further evidence of the benefit of their innovations could actually slow down therapeutic progress and add to the cost of medical care.

However, the flavour of the debate was influenced in favour of the development of health indicators or health profiles by the fact that four of their protagonists were actually describing the practical use of such measures from their own experience. Buxton, McEwen, Paterson and Rosser were all able to quote personal examples of the use of socio-economic 'instruments'. Furthermore, the range of application of this work in so many different fields of medicine was impressive. Probably the most crucial

163

experience is that of SmithKline Beckman with auranofin, described by Mort Paterson. This is the case of a pharmaceutical company which has put a very substantial investment into an attempt to measure the social benefits of its new medicine, to supplement the traditional clinical measures. It was clear from the discussion that there are the usual methodological reasons why this may not in fact provide the evidence which SmithKline Beckman hope will emerge. In particular, the relatively short time-scale over which the assessment is being carried out may not be long enough to demonstrate the social benefits. Nevertheless, the fact is that this major international pharmaceutical company has decided to back the principle of trying to demonstrate social, in addition to medical, benefits during a controlled clinical trial. Other pharmaceutical firms will obviously watch with fascination the outcome of this very far-sighted experiment.

In answer to the first question, therefore, it is probably still too soon to say unequivocally that the measurement of the social benefits of therapy will prove to be desirable. However, those who have had practical experience in the field have confidence that the answer will be positive. It will certainly not be the first time in the history of medicine if the medical and pharmaceutical sceptics at this early stage are eventually proved wrong. Progress in medicine has never been without controversy and debate, and in this sense the differing points of view expressed in these papers and in the discussion at Brunel are a healthy sign of the continuing scientific progress of medicine.

My second question is whether such measurements are feasible. The answer in this case is undoubtedly 'yes'. I have already pointed out that several of the papers in this volume describe practical experiences with use of 'health profiles' or 'health indicators'. However, Alan Williams' paper provoked a thoughtful discussion on a more important issue. Given that it is feasible to measure the health status of individuals, is it meaningful to do so? This debate centred on the concept of 'quality adjusted life years' – or QALY's for short (Mort Paterson at one stage transposed these QALY's into 'Wellies', suggesting the muddy nature of the ground being trodden in the discussion). In Alan Williams' theoretical model, each person has an expected span of QALY's. Disabling diseases naturally reduce the score of QALY's by impairing the quality of life, and fatal diseases reduce the score by restricting the total number of years. Medical intervention, on the other hand, can improve the natural score either by prolonging life or by improving its quality.

David Goldberg very cogently pointed out that a person's natural span of QUALY's was, in practice, impossible to determine because medical procedures would always alter what would otherwise have happened. To this, Alan Williams countered that it was not necessary to take as the baseline the expected value of QALY's without *any* medical care, but only with and without particular intervention(s). To me, at least, this intellectual exercise seems attractive. It provides a conceptual framework in which the quality of life can be integrated with the increasingly meaningless measure of the length of life in isolation. Indeed Rachel Rosser's work suggests that death may not be the zero point in the scale of wellbeing. In some situations extra years of life may actually be so intolerably horrible that they subtract from the total score of wellbeing. In this situation a 'quality adjusted life year' will have a negative value.

This leads on to the third question, of whether 'health profiles' are in fact more meaningful than 'health indices' such as the QALY. The latter attempt to produce a single scale, by aggregating measurements of many different aspects of performance and experience. By contrast, the concept of the health profile accepts that such disparate measurements as degrees of depression and degrees of mobility cannot be aggregated. A health profile therefore sets out to describe a person's situation in quantitative terms, but accepts the quantification for different measurements without adding them together. The advantage argued for the 'profile' approach is that it can provide a more disease specific basis from which to compare an individual's progress over time, with or without therapy. The SmithKline Beckman experiment and Martin Buxton's work on heart transplants both use profiles, the former using an index as well. In addition a standard profile such as that developed at Nottingham can be used to compare and describe the different impact of different diseases.

Thus however intellectually attractive the concept of a single index such as the QALY may be, it seems that for the present at least profiles are likely to prove more readily acceptable instruments to measure wellbeing than single indices. This, of course, means that it is impossible to provide a single measurement which can be translated into monetary terms and equated to the monetary cost of therapy in a cost-benefit equation. The choice in allocation of resources thus remains a matter of judgement rather than the solution of an arithmetical equation. To those involved in health care planning this must come as no surprise, and indeed perhaps as something of a relief. The idea that economists could solve the conundrum of how geriatric care should be balanced against high technology medicine for the middle aged would be a rather frightening one. But this in no way negates the validity of attempting to quantify the benefits of albeit very disparate forms of medical care.

The final question was 'how soon should assessments be carried out?' In the sense of the proper stage in the development of a new therapy to carry out evaluation, the question was best answered by Martin Buxton: 'It is always too soon, until it is suddenly too late'. At the early stages of development, the appropriate use of the therapy may not have been determined and experience with it may be too limited to make it fully effective. Thus in measuring the benefits at this stage one may be doing less than justice to the eventual potential from the procedure or the medicine. On the other hand, once a procedure has become well-established and its benefits generally acknowledged, it may no longer be ethical to undertake a controlled comparison between the proven treatment and some undoubtedly inferior alternative (such as placebo therapy). In the case of both auranofin and heart transplants, Mort Paterson and Martin Buxton have opted for evaluation at an early stage. Given the dilemma set out above, this is probably the right choice. On the other hand, representatives from the pharmaceutical industry argued strongly that it is still much too soon for the registration or pricing authorities to expect this sort of evaluation to be undertaken on new medicines before they are marketed. Here, again, I can only agree.

This raises the other interpretation of the question 'When?' This is the issue of how soon – if ever – should the use of health profiles or health indicators become routine in the evaluation and planning of medical care. This must be a matter for the crystal gazers. To clutch a good round figure out of the air, perhaps in another ten years the principle of socio-economic evaluation of new therapies may be fairly generally accepted. But even by the mid-1990s it will probably still be too soon for such evaluation to be expected routinely before a new medicine or a new therapy is introduced. The papers in this volume have indicated that the measurement of social benefits is still at an embryonic stage.

One can draw an analogy here with the introduction of the double-blind randomised controlled trial in the *clinical* evaluation of new therapies. It was soon after the Second World War that the principle of the double-blind trial was generally introduced for the assessment of new medicines in Britain. Twenty years later – in the 1970s – Professor Archie Cochrane in his classic book 'Effectiveness and Efficiency; random reflections on health services' lamented that the findings of randomised controlled trials had had so little influence on the patterns of other aspects of medical care. It will be interesting to see if social measurements of benefits also come first to be introduced for pharmaceuticals – again for the reasons which I argued in the opening chapter. It seems at least possible that pharmaceutical companies may soon be turning to health economists for expert advice, in the same way as they turned to clinicians and clinical pharmacologists for help in the systematic medical evaluation of their new medicines thirty years ago.

Certainly, however, this will, and should, be a slow process. At present, the socio-economic evaluation of medical care is in an experimental stage. For one thing, there is only a very, very limited pool of expertise in the field at present. If the discipline of the measurement of social benefits of therapy is to expand, specialists will need to be educated in the necessary techniques and skills. However, pharmaceutical companies, and doctors and health care planners, should, at this stage, be aware of the potential developments indicated by some of the contributors to this book.

Like the controlled clinical trial itself, this could become an appropriate area of special expertise for Britain, In the 1970s, much of the thinking on this subject was undertaken in North America. Nevertheless, the contributors to this volume indicate that Britain also has much to offer in this field. However slowly and tentatively the subject moves forward, it seems likely that the measurement of the social benefits of therapy will become an increasingly important aspect of medical care in the years ahead. Perhaps then, as I suggested in the Foreword, this book may become a landmark in Britain's involvement in this emerging discipline.

Index